PRENTICE-HALL BIOLOGICAL SCIENCE SERIES
William D. McElroy and Carl P. Swanson, *Editors*

BIOCHEMICAL SYSTEMATICS,* by Ralph E. Alston and B. L. Turner
CLASSIC PAPERS IN GENETICS, by James A. Peters
EXPERIMENTAL BIOLOGY, by Richard W. Van Norman
FOUNDATIONS OF EXPERIMENTAL EMBRYOLOGY, by Benjamin H. Willier
  and Jane M. Oppenheimer
MECHANISMS OF BODY FUNCTIONS, by Dexter M. Easton
MILESTONES IN MICROBIOLOGY, by Thomas D. Brock
PAPERS ON HUMAN GENETICS, by Samuel H. Boyer, IV
POISONOUS PLANTS OF THE UNITED STATES AND CANADA, by John M.
  Kingsbury
PRINCIPLES OF BIOLOGY, by Neal D. Buffaloe
SELECTED BOTANICAL PAPERS, by Irving W. Knobloch
SELECTED PAPERS ON VIROLOGY, by Nicholas Hahon
A SYNTHESIS OF EVOLUTIONARY THEORY, by Herbert H. Ross

Concepts of Modern Biology Series

BEHAVIORAL ASPECTS OF ECOLOGY,* by Peter H. Klopfer
MOLECULAR BIOLOGY: GENES AND THE CHEMICAL CONTROL OF LIVING
  CELLS, by J. M. Barry

Foundations of Modern Biology Series

ADAPTATION, by Bruce Wallace and A. M. Srb
ANIMAL BEHAVIOR, by Vincent Dethier and Eliot Stellar
ANIMAL DIVERSITY, by Earl D. Hanson
ANIMAL PHYSIOLOGY, by Knut Schmidt-Neilsen
THE CELL, by Carl P. Swanson
CELL PHYSIOLOGY AND BIOCHEMISTRY, by William D. McElroy
CHEMICAL BACKGROUND FOR THE BIOLOGICAL SCIENCES, by Emil H. White
GROWTH AND DEVELOPMENT, by Maurice Sussman
HEREDITY, by David M. Bonner and Stanley E. Mills
THE LIFE OF THE GREEN PLANT, by Arthur W. Galston
MAN IN NATURE, by Marston Bates
THE PLANT KINGDOM, by Harold C. Bold

* These titles are also in the Prentice-Hall International Series in Biological
Science. Prentice-Hall, Inc.; Prentice-Hall International, United Kingdom and
Eire; Prentice-Hall of Canada, Ltd., Canada.

CONCEPTS OF MODERN BIOLOGY SERIES

William D. McElroy and Carl P. Swanson, *Editors*

Molecular Biology: Genes and the
Chemical Control of Living Cells
by J. M. Barry, University Lecturer,
University of Oxford, England.
Published by Prentice-Hall, Inc.,
Englewood Cliffs, New Jersey

PRENTICE-HALL INTERNATIONAL, INC., *London*
PRENTICE-HALL OF AUSTRALIA, PTY., LTD., *Sydney*
PRENTICE-HALL OF CANADA, LTD., *Toronto*
PRENTICE-HALL OF INDIA (PRIVATE) LTD., *New Delhi*
PRENTICE-HALL OF JAPAN, INC., *Tokyo*
PRENTICE-HALL DE MEXICO, S.A., *Mexico City*

Second printing...........September, 1964

To M. J. McC.

Concepts of Modern Biology Series   The main body of biological literature consists of the research paper, the review article or book, the textbook, and the reference book, all of which are too often limited in scope by circumstances other than those dictated by the subject matter or the author. Unlike their usual predecessors, the books in this series, CONCEPTS OF MODERN BIOLOGY, are exceptional in their obvious freedom from such artificial limitations as are often imposed by course demands and subject restrictions.

Today the gulf of ignorance is widening, not because of a diminished capacity for learning, but because of the quantity of information being unearthed, most of which comes in small, analytical bits, undigested and unrelated. The role of the synthesizer, therefore, increases in importance, for it is he who must take the giant steps, and carry us along with him; he must go beyond his individual observations and conclusions, to assess his work and that of others in a broader context and with fresh insight. Hopefully, the CONCEPTS OF MODERN BIOLOGY SERIES provides the opportunity for decreasing the gulf of ignorance by increasing the quantity of information and quality of presentation. As editors of the Prentice-Hall Biological Science Series, we are convinced that such volumes occupy an important place in the education of the practicing and prospective teacher and investigator.

WILLIAM D. MC ELROY

CARL P. SWANSON

Preface The purpose of this book is to introduce, in a simple way, discoveries in the subject which has become known as molecular biology—discoveries which show precisely how inherited differences between one living organism and another are founded on differences in the structure of chemical molecules. It is hoped that the book will be intelligible even to readers who have only the basic facts of chemistry and biology clear in their minds—in particular, how compounds are formed by combination of the atoms of elements, and how living organisms are composed of cells that reproduce by division.

The discoveries of molecular biology give a fascinating insight into the workings of living cells, but they have also a more general importance. Before Darwin published his "Origin of Species" it was reasonable for a man of good education and judgment to hold that each species of animal and plant had originally been placed on earth by an act of special creation. Since that time, no reasonable man can believe this, for the evidence is overwhelming that all animals and plants have evolved from one or a few primitive ancestors by the interaction of the forces of nature. The conclusions of molecular biologists have a comparable philosophical importance. As recently as the 1930's, many reputable scientists were vitalists: they believed that unknown vital forces operate in living cells, and that the mere interaction of their component molecules according to the familiar laws of science would not make them live. These scientists knew that many of the chemical reactions in cells are similar to those that occur in the laboratory. But it seemed to them highly improbable that the fundamental property of cells, namely, their ability to reproduce like cells, would ever be explained in chemical terms. Recent discoveries in molecular biology have largely produced this explanation, and so rendered vitalist theories about the function of living cells difficult to maintain.

In this book certain leading experiments, that together reveal the chemical foundations of genetics, have been selected and described in detail. The conclusions reached are supported by many other excellent experiments by workers whose names have not been mentioned. It is hoped that this omission will simplify the beginner's approach to the subject, and enable him to grasp these other experiments in the more detailed accounts mentioned at the end of the book under "Selected Readings."

J. M. BARRY

Contents

Proteins and Nucleic Acids

1

1 PROTEINS

Living organisms, like all non-living things, are composed of molecules which are built up from the atoms of elements. The weight of a living organism is the sum of the weights of the molecules of which it is composed. In this chapter, the structure of proteins and nucleic acids will be described. They are peculiar to living organisms, and it is on variations in the structure of their molecules that inherited differences between living organisms are founded.

Proteins, which we shall consider first, were isolated in the last century from living organisms and were recognized as a group of compounds whose molecules have related, but distinct, structures. They were all found to contain the elements carbon, hydrogen, oxygen, nitrogen, and sulphur in roughly the same proportions, but to differ from one another in certain properties, such as the ease with which they are precipitated with acids and salt solutions. It was soon discovered that the molecular weights of proteins are very large, and that their molecules must contain some thousands of atoms. The problem of discovering the precise molecular structure of any protein appeared difficult, that is, of discovering precisely how the component atoms are linked together to form the molecule.

A start to solving this problem was made when it was discovered that all proteins are built up from a limited number of smaller molecules called amino acids, into which they disintegrate when heated with hydrochloric acid. It is now known that twenty kinds of amino acid occur in normal proteins. Their structures are shown in Fig. 1. It is seen that all except one have a carboxyl (–COOH) group and an amino (–NH$_2$) group linked in the same carbon atom. To this carbon is also linked a hydrogen atom and another organic group by which one amino acid is distinguished from the next. The structure of the one exception, proline, is closely related to that of the others. It has a carboxyl and an amino (–N–H) group linked to a common carbon atom. Some protein molecules contain all twenty kinds of amino acid while others contain a few less.

The manner in which amino acids are linked together to form protein molecules was established around 1900 by the great German chemist, Emil Fischer. He showed that the carboxyl group of one amino acid can react with the amino group of another; water is eliminated, and a bond known as a peptide bond is formed (Fig. 2, page 4). This type of reaction does not necessarily end with the joining of two amino acids, since the molecule which is formed has a free carboxyl group at one end and a

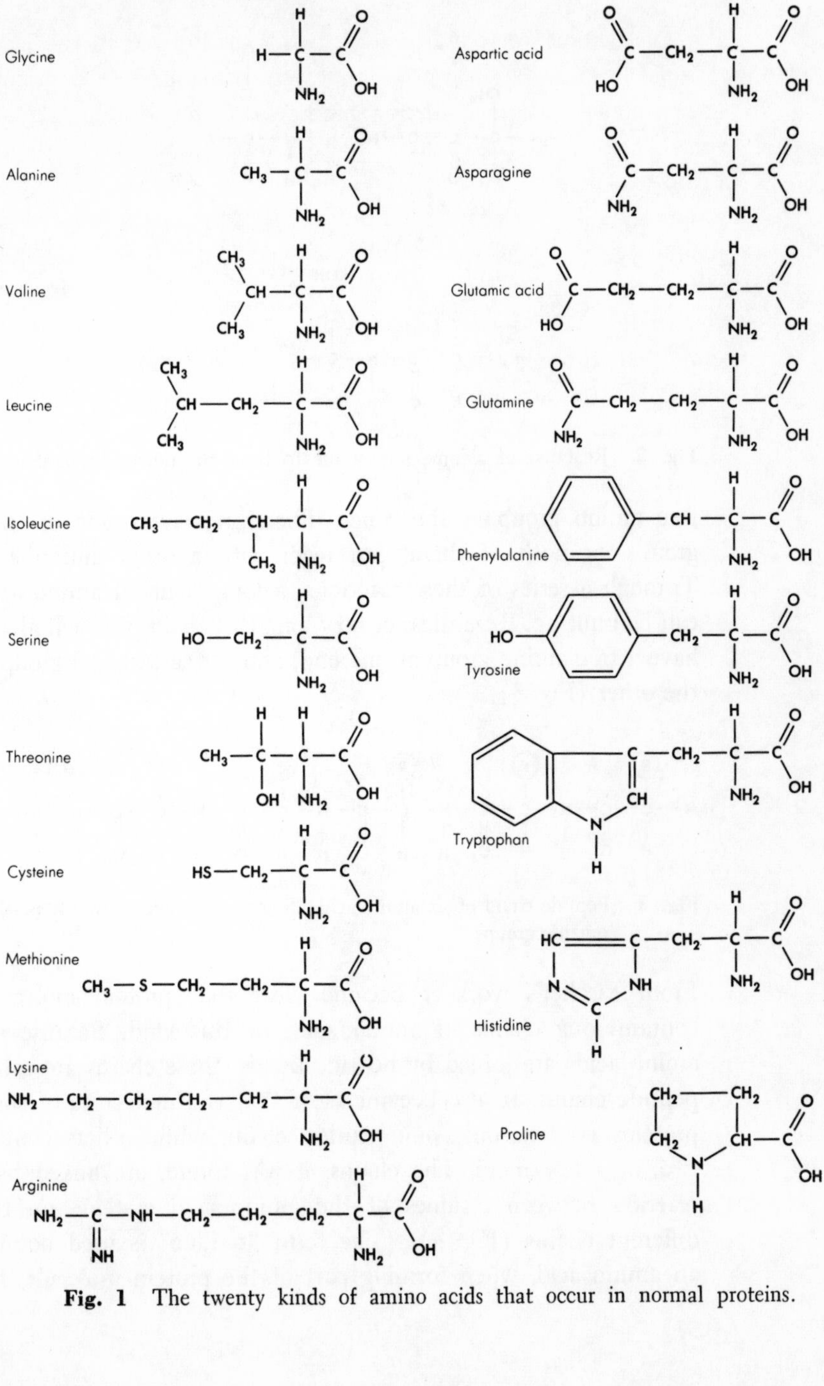

Fig. 1 The twenty kinds of amino acids that occur in normal proteins.

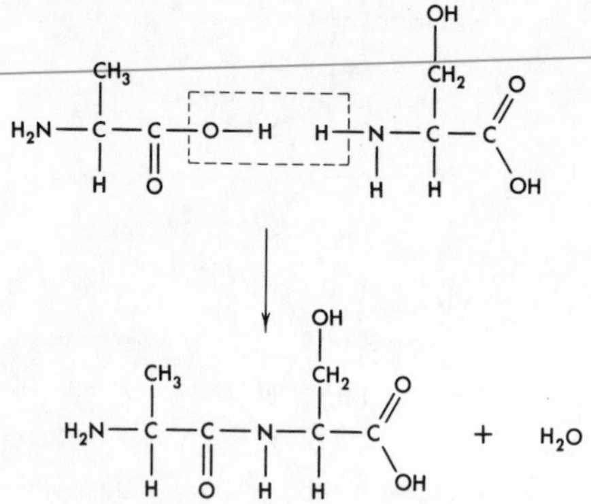

Fig. 2 Reaction of alanine and serine to form the dipeptide alanlyserine.

free amino group at the other. Therefore, either one of these groups, or both of them, can react with another amino acid. Through a series of these reactions, a long chain of amino acids can be built up. Regardless of how long this chain is, it will always have a free amino group at one end, and a free carboxyl group at the other (Fig. 3).

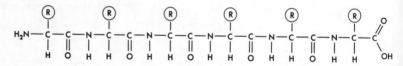

Fig. 3 Peptide chain of six amino acids. R represents one of twenty possible organic groups.

From Fischer's work it became clear that protein molecules contain long chains of amino acids of this kind. Because the amino acids are joined by peptide bonds, these chains are called peptide chains. It also became clear that the molecules of some proteins contain only one peptide chain, while others contain two, or a few more. The chains, it was found, are linked by a reaction between residues of the amino acid cysteine on two different chains (Fig. 4). (The term "residue" is used because an amino acid, when forming part of the protein molecule, has

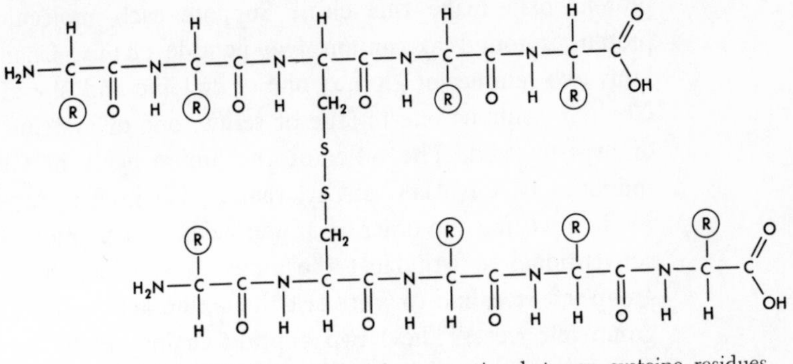

Fig. 4 Two peptide chains linked by a reaction between cysteine residues. R represents any one of nineteen other organic groups.

lost two hydrogen atoms and an oxygen atom, and has also lost its identity as a molecule.) The molecular weights of proteins showed that each peptide chain in a protein molecule must normally be composed of a hundred or more amino acid residues.

With these discoveries, the interest of chemists in the structure of proteins largely ended. By the start of the twentieth century, organic chemistry had become hardened into a clearly defined subject with set limits of interest. Proteins lay outside these limits, largely because their purity could not be demonstrated by the classical methods of organic chemistry. As a result, the study of protein structure was left to biochemists, and it was they who were able to make the most triumphant discovery in organic chemistry of the century, the discovery of the precise arrangement of amino acids in the molecule of a protein.

2 SOME MISCONCEIVED THEORIES OF PROTEIN STRUCTURE

The task of completely discovering the structure of a particular protein involves finding the number of peptide chains in the molecule, the number of residues of each kind of amino acid in each chain, the order in which these amino acids are arranged in each chain, and precisely how the different chains are linked. A hypothetical, and highly simplified, example of a protein may make this clear. Suppose each molecule of the protein is found to contain two peptide chains. Chain 1 contains two residues of glycine, one of cysteine and one of alanine. Chain 2 contains one residue of serine, one of cysteine and one of aspartic acid. The order of the amino acids in Chain 1 is found to be Gly-Ala-Cyst-Gly; that in Chain 2 is Asp-Cyst-Ser. (When writing the order of amino acids in a peptide chain it is conventional to write first the amino acid which has its $-NH_2$ group left free, and to write last the amino acid with its $-COOH$ group left free.) These two peptide chains are linked by cross linkages between the cysteine residues. The complete structure of this hypothetical protein is shown in Fig. 5.

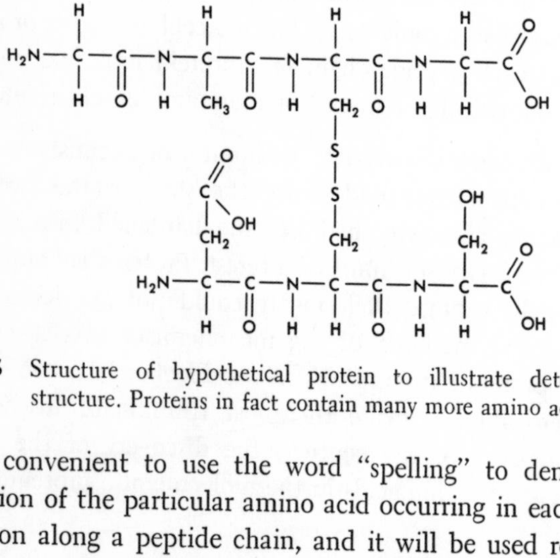

Fig. 5 Structure of hypothetical protein to illustrate determination of structure. Proteins in fact contain many more amino acids.

It is convenient to use the word "spelling" to denote the description of the particular amino acid occurring in each successive position along a peptide chain, and it will be used repeatedly in this book. The "spelling" of Chain 1 in the above example is thus, Gly-Ala-Cyst-Gly. This usage is founded on the similarity of a peptide chain to a word. A word is a chain of letters of which there are twenty-six kinds. A peptide is a chain of amino acids of which there are twenty kinds.

In the example just discussed it has been assumed that a protein can be isolated and assigned a precise structure; in other words, that a sample of a protein can be "pure" by the definition of the organic chemist, in that it is a collection of identical molecules. Protein molecules are, however, far larger than this simplified model. It might seem improbable that a living cell could repeatedly make peptide chains containing a hundred or so amino acids without the slightest variation in chain length or spelling. To many biochemists around 1945, when little progress had been made in finding the precise structure of proteins, this did, in fact, seem highly improbable. They suggested, therefore, that a "pure" protein would always have slight variations in the spelling of its peptide chains from one molecule to the next; because of this variation, the problem of protein structure could never be solved precisely.

Another important group of biochemists took, at this time, a more optimistic view of protein structure, in fact, as we now know, an overly optimistic view. They suggested that the different molecules of a pure protein contain peptide chains of identical length and spelling. Moreover, they claimed that analyses of proteins suggested that a fundamental simplicity exists in their spelling, namely, that, *"in every protein, each amino acid residue is distributed throughout the entire length of the peptide chain at constant intervals."* For example, it was claimed that silk protein contains residues of the amino acids tyrosine, alanine, and glycine in the ratio 1:4:8, and it was suggested that each molecule of the protein consists of a single peptide chain with the spelling:

-T-G-A-G-X-G-A-G-X-G-A-G-X-G-A-G-

repeated again and again over its entire length (where T is tyrosine, G is glycine, A is alanine, and X is some other amino acid). In actual fact the ratios, found in analyses of different proteins, between the number of residues of the different kinds of amino acid were not very close to the small whole numbers which the theory required. But this, it was claimed, could be due to impurity of the proteins and inadequate analytical methods.

More recent analyses of pure proteins with adequate techniques show that these simple ratios do not exist, and the theory has been abandoned.

Recent experiments, that will now be described, have shown that both these theories of protein structure were incorrect. Proteins can be pure by the definition of the organic chemist and, in spite of the large size of their molecules, the spelling of the peptide chains in one molecule is identical to that in the next. The peptide chains, however, contain no repeating sequences of amino acids. These facts of protein structure are important to the correct functioning of living cells. The reason why will become clearer in later chapters, but for the moment it can be illustrated by the analogy which likens a peptide chain to a word composed of amino acid "letters." If a word was never spelled in the same way twice, communication would be imprecise; while, if all words had to be spelled in a rigidly repeating sequence of letters, the possible number of words would be unnecessarily limited. The precise and detailed communication between cell nucleus and cytoplasm is based on unvarying spelling in the peptide chains of each protein, without repeating sequences of amino acids.

3   THE TRUE STRUCTURE OF PROTEINS REVEALED

Until about twenty years ago, proteins were looked on with almost mystical awe by many biochemists. To regard proteins as normal organic compounds, and to attempt to discover their structure, took great courage. This was, in fact, done by A. C. Chibnall and his colleagues in the biochemistry department of Cambridge University; and one member of this group, F. Sanger, brought their work brilliantly to fruition by discovering, between 1945 and 1955, the arrangement of all the amino acids in the protein, insulin, the hormone taken by diabetics. Sanger and his colleagues chose insulin because its molecule is relatively simple, and contains only fifty-one amino acid residues. They assumed that every molecule in a pure sample of insulin is identical to the next—an assumption that was proved to be justified by the rational results they obtained from their analyses.

Sanger's work was founded on the newly discovered technique of paper chromatography which enables amino acids and pep-tides to be separated from one another very simply. The follow-ing is an example of this technique. A sheet of filter paper about twelve inches square is cut out. At one corner is put a very small drop of a solution containing a mixture of amino acids, and the wet spot is allowed to dry. The paper is then suspended in a tank which has a thin layer of a solvent, such as a solution of butyl alcohol and acetic acid, at the bottom. One of the two edges of the paper which has the amino acid spot at one end is allowed to dip into this solution. The tank is closed and left for some hours until the solvent has been sucked up almost to the opposite edge of the paper. It is then removed and left to dry. When the solvent moves up the filter paper the amino acids are carried up with it. However, different amino acids move up at different speeds, depending on their relative affinities for the surface of the filter paper and the solvent. As a result, when the solution reaches the top of the paper, the amino acids have moved to different and characteristic spots vertically above the original spot. Certain amino acids happen to move to the same position, and in order to separate these from one another, the whole process is repeated. In this second run a different solvent is used—for example, a solution of phenol; and the edge of the paper along which the amino acids have now become distributed is placed in this solvent. The result of this "two-dimensional" chromatography is that the amino acids become distributed in small circles in different and characteristic positions on the paper. They are made visible by spraying the paper with a solution of ninhydrin which reacts with amino acids and peptides to give a blue color. By this technique, the amino acids which occur in a protein can be identified and their relative amounts roughly estimated. Also, peptides of unknown structure can be separated from one another.

Sanger's work also depended on a second technique that will reveal which particular amino acid lies at the end of a peptide chain with its –NH$_2$ group free. He found that when a protein is dissolved in sodium bicarbonate solution and an alcoholic solution of 2:4 dinitrofluorobenzene is added, a molecule of this

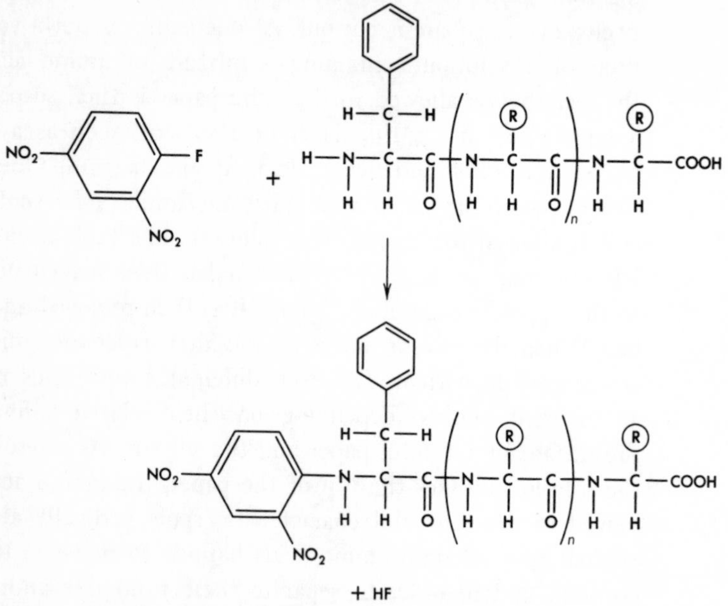

Fig. 6 Sanger's reagent, 2:4 dinitrofluorobenzene, reacting with phenylalanine residue at end of protein chain.

compound attaches itself to the free –NH$_2$ group at the end of each peptide chain (Fig. 6). The important part of this discovery was that the compound remains attached to this group after the protein is hydrolyzed into its individual amino acids with hydrochloric acid. The resulting dinitrophenyl amino acid from the end of the peptide chain can be easily isolated because it is soluble in ether; and its particular kind of amino acid can be identified by paper chromatography. If more than one dinitro-phenyl amino acid is obtained, then the protein must have more than one amino acid chain per molecule.

Sanger treated insulin with this reagent, and then hydrolyzed it into its component amino acids. He found that the dinitro-phenyl derivatives of glycine and phenylalanine were formed in the amounts expected if insulin has two peptide chains, one beginning at the free $-NH_2$ end with glycine, and the other with phenylalanine. By treating insulin with an oxidizing agent Sanger was able to break the linkage between the two peptides and iso-late each separately. He then set about to discover the spelling of each.

If a protein is heated with hydrochloric acid to 37°C instead of to boiling, it is not hydrolyzed completely into its component amino acids. The peptide bonds are broken slowly and a mixture of an enormous number of peptide fragments is formed. But since certain peptide links in the protein are broken more rapidly than others, certain fragments of the protein will predominate over the others. Sanger warmed each of the peptide chains of insulin in this way and was able to isolate certain peptide frag-ments chemically pure. He set about finding the spelling of these peptides in the following way: if a peptide contained only two amino acids, he was able to establish its spelling im-mediately by reacting it with 2:4 dinitrofluorobenzene: the amino acid which reacted with this reagent was the one which had its $-NH_2$ group free. If a peptide contained three amino acids, the one with its $-NH_2$ group free could again be identified, but the order of the other two remained unknown. The tripeptide was then warmed with hydrochloric acid, and one of the two pos-sible dipeptides was isolated. Its spelling was determined, and from this the spelling of the tripeptide could be deduced. The spelling of larger peptides was found by an extension of this method.

From the spelling of overlapping fragments of the peptide chains of insulin, Sanger was able to deduce the spelling of each chain.

For example, the chain beginning in glycine yielded the fragments: Ser–Leu–Tyr, and Leu–Tyr–Glu. Sanger concluded that they were derived from the following sequence in the peptide of insulin: Ser–Leu–Tyr–Glu. The principle is the same as if we knew that a word of seven letters contained the sequences INS, SULI, and LIN. The word is clearly INSULIN.

Sanger had isolated the two peptide chains of insulin by first oxidizing the protein and so breaking the linkages between one residue of the amino acid cysteine and another. One peptide chain of insulin contained four residues of cysteine and the other contained two. It was now necessary to discover which of these residues are linked into pairs. He discovered this by submitting the intact protein to mild hydrolysis, and isolating fragments containing only one of the three pairs of cysteine residues. From the spelling of these fragments he was able to deduce the spelling of the complete insulin molecule (Fig. 7). For this work, Sanger has been awarded the Nobel Prize for chemistry.

4 MORE RECENT METHODS OF DISCOVERING THE STRUCTURE OF PROTEINS

Sanger's methods of determining the spelling of peptide chains were slow and arduous. The mild hydrolysis with acid gives a complex mixture of fragments, and pure peptides from overlapping regions of the original chain are difficult to isolate. In recent years the techniques have been greatly improved, and the structures of more than ten proteins are now known. The most important advance has been the use of certain enzymes which are secreted by the digestive tracts of mammals for the purpose of breaking down the proteins of food. These enzymes break the linkages only between certain kinds of amino acids in protein chains, and the most useful is trypsin which can be isolated from the pancreases of cattle. This enzyme breaks only peptide linkages between the carboxyl groups of lysine or arginine, and the amino groups of any other amino acid. As a result, it severs a long peptide into a limited number of fragments from

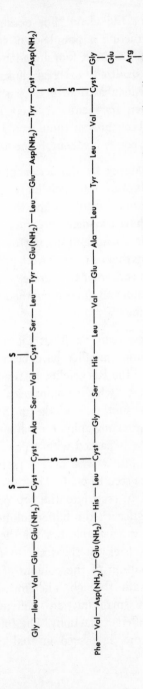

Fig. 7   Structure of insulin of ox.

adjacent regions of the chain. For example, the protein ribonuclease, whose structure is now known, contains a single chain of 124 amino acids. Of these, four are arginine and ten are lysine. If the protein is oxidized, to break linkages between cysteine residues, and then incubated with trypsin for a few hours, it is broken into thirteen fragments. If every bond involving lysine and arginine had been broken there would be fifteen fragments. In fact, two of the bonds involving lysine are not susceptible.

The fragments produced by the action of trypsin can, if necessary, be cleanly broken into smaller ones by other digestive enzymes. It is then not difficult to find the spelling of these small fragments. Since these fragments are from adjacent segments of the original peptide chain, and do not overlap, the problem remains of assembling them in the correct order. This order can be found by breaking the original peptide into different fragments with different enzymes and discovering their spelling in the regions of lysine and arginine.

Also, in the last few years, methods for separating amino acids and peptides from one another have been improved. S. Moore and W. H. Stein, of the Rockefeller Institute in New York, have developed methods by which amino acids and peptides can be separated from one another, and the quantities of each exactly determined, by chromatography on columns of resin. A tall, cylindrical glass tube is packed with a powdered resin suspended in a buffered salt solution. The tube is perforated at the base to allow the solution to seep through. The mixture of amino acids or peptides is allowed to seep into the top of this column and is then washed through with the buffer solution. The amino acids and peptides have varying affinities for the resin surface. They are, therefore, held back by the resin to different extents and emerge from the bottom of the column after different volumes of buffer have been run through. Therefore, if the emerging solution is divided into small fractions, different amino acids and peptides occur in different fractions. The fractions in which each amino acid occurs are discovered in trial experiments, and the quantity of amino acid in these fractions is determined by analysis. Stein and Moore have built an apparatus which makes this separation and analysis completely automatic. If the mixture of amino acids from a protein is put on top of the column of resin, the apparatus may be left to its own devices for a few days. At the end of this predetermined period, it will present its operator with a graph showing the quantities and kinds of the different amino acids in the original mixture. Using enzymic hydrolysis, and chromatography on resins, Stein and Moore have discovered the complete spelling of the protein ribonuclease from the pancreas of the ox (Fig. 8). It is seen to contain only one peptide chain, different parts of which are linked by bonds between pairs of cysteine residues.

From the results of this, and other discoveries of the spelling of proteins, certain conclusions can be drawn about their structure. It is clear that in a sample of a pure protein every molecule is, in fact, identical to the next. Surprising as it may seem, there is no misspelling from one molecule to the next. Moreover, along each peptide chain the amino acids appear to be in a complete jumble, that is, a certain amino acid does not appear at regular intervals along the chain, nor do two amino acids appear to occur next to one another more often than would be expected by

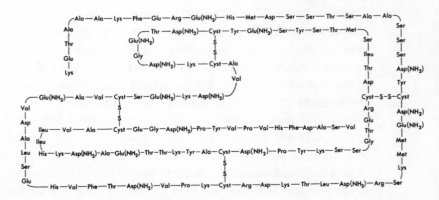

Fig. 8   Structure of pancreatic ribonuclease of ox.

chance. Most proteins differ completely in their spelling, but that of closely related proteins can be very similar. Sanger and his helpers have studied, as well as ox insulin, insulin from the pig, sheep, horse, and whale. The spelling of each is identical except for a sequence of three amino acids which differs from one species to the next—we are reminded of slight differences of spelling of the same word in different languages, such as color, colour, couleur and colore.

5   THE THREE-DIMENSIONAL STRUCTURE OF PROTEINS

From what has been said so far it might be thought that the peptide chains of proteins are free to indulge in snakelike movements, and can assume a large number of configurations. In fact, it appears that, even in solution, they cannot. The molecules of most pure proteins, as well as having identical amino acid chains, are apparently coiled into structures of identical shape. This three-dimensional structure has recently been discovered in great detail for two proteins by the physical method of X-ray diffraction.

This method is based on the physical principle of diffraction. When a light wave strikes the edge of an obstacle it undergoes diffraction, that is, it breaks into secondary waves which radiate in all directions from the obstacle. If a beam of parallel light waves of a single wave length is shone through a glass plate, on which a series of parallel lines have been etched, diffraction occurs at these lines. Light waves leave this "diffraction grating" in all directions. The waves which leave from one line can undergo interference with those that leave from adjacent lines, that is, if the crests of one wave coincide with the crests of the next they will reinforce one another to give brighter light, and if the crests and troughs coincide, darkness will result. Therefore, if the light leaving the glass plate falls onto a screen it will give dark and light bands. If the wave length of the light is known, the distance between the lines on the grating can be simply calculated from the distance between the bands on the screen.

In order to obtain these diffraction bands, the distance between the lines on the grating must be of the same order as the wave length of the light which is used.

Pure crystals contain identical molecules packed in a regular order. Because of this regular packing, the atoms in a crystal lie in planes which can act like the lines on a diffraction grating. The distance between these planes varies with the direction from which the crystal is viewed. The simplest way to understand why this is so is to consider a square forest of identical trees, planted ten feet apart, in rows which are twenty feet apart. If the forest is viewed from one side, the trees will form planes twenty feet apart, while from the adjacent side the planes will be ten feet apart. Viewed from a corner the planes will be just over seven feet apart. In a crystal, the distance between the planes formed by the atoms varies with the position of viewing not only in two dimensions, as here, but also in three dimensions; and it varies most frequently when the crystal is composed of large and complicated molecules.

A crystal is, therefore, like a three-dimensional diffraction grating, but the distance between the planes is too small to diffract visible light and crystals will only diffract X rays, which have a very short wave length. If a beam of X rays is shined onto a crystal and the emerging rays are allowed to fall onto a photographic plate, dark and light diffraction spots result. The distance between these spots changes as the crystal is rotated in three dimensions. By making the correct measurements, the distances between the lines of atoms in the crystal can be calculated; from these, the distances between the atoms in the component molecule can be derived.

Protein molecules are extremely complex and, when their crystals are rotated, they produce thousands of distinct diffraction patterns. Hence, the calculation of the distances between the component atoms is extremely complicated. About twenty-five years ago, X ray diffraction patterns were first obtained from protein crystals, but the problem of deducing the structure of the molecules was too complex to be solved. But, in the last ten years an important advance in technique has simplified the calculation of the results to a level which can be handled by fast electronic computers. Using these methods, M. F. Perutz and J. C. Kendrew and their colleagues at Cambridge University, after thousands of measurements and calculations, have deduced in great detail the three-dimensional structures of two proteins: hemoglobin from blood, and myoglobin from muscle.

The more diffraction measurements that are made on a protein crystal, the more detailed is the structure that can be deduced. In Fig. 9 is shown a model made by Kendrew and colleagues from their first calculations of the structure of a myoglobin molecule. The outline of the protein chain can be seen clearly, but no details of the atoms of which the chain is composed are visible.

Recently, Perutz and Kendrew have made very detailed analyses of the structure of hemoglobin and myoglobin which show not only how the protein chain is coiled, but even distinguish, from one another, the individual amino acids which make up the protein chain. Therefore, by one series of diffraction measurements on a protein crystal it is possible to discover not only the three-dimensional coiling of the protein chain, but also its spelling. Hence, with proteins that form suitable crystals these physical studies can now compete with chemical studies of protein structure. For these experiments, Perutz and Kendrew were awarded the Nobel Prize in 1962.

6 NUCLEIC ACIDS

Nucleic acids, like proteins, can be extracted from living cells, and are of two distinct types: ribonucleic acids (abbreviated to RNA) and deoxyribonucleic acids (abbreviated to DNA). Their

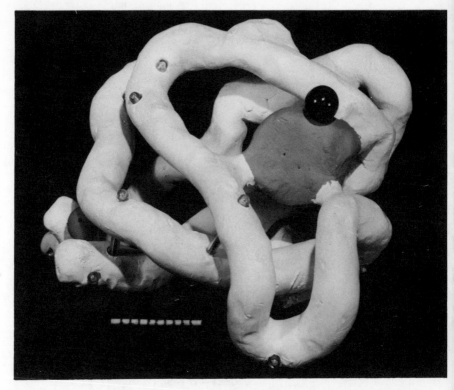

Fig. 9   Model of molecule of protein myoglobin. The white coil represents
the peptide chain, and the grey disc to the upper left, a molecule
of heme with which the protein is associated. The two balls represent
the positions of heavy atoms which are attached to the protein in
determining its structure. The scale at the bottom shows ten
Angstrom units. (Courtesy Dr. J. C. Kendrew.)

molecules are very large, but once again, the problem of discovering their structure is made simpler by the fact that they
break down, when dissolved in a solution of sodium hydroxide,
into a mixture of smaller molecules. These are called nucleotides,
and their structures were laboriously discovered in the first half
of the twentieth century.

This disintegration of nucleic acids into nucleotides reminds us

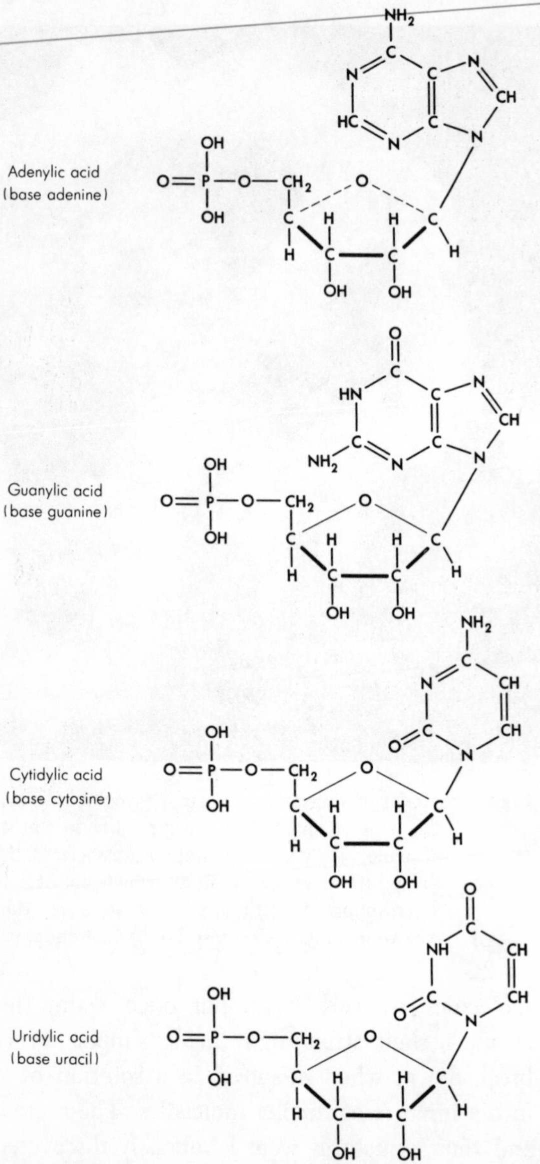

Fig. 10 The four nucleotides of RNA. In the center of each nucleotide is the ring of the sugar ribose containing four carbon atoms and one oxygen atom.

of the disintegration of proteins into amino acids, and in fact nucleic acid molecules are long chains of linked nucleotide residues. But, whereas a protein molecule contains up to twenty kinds of amino acid, a nucleic acid contains normally only four kinds of nucleotide. Moreover, RNA and DNA yield nucleotides of different types. It is as if one group of words were composed only of the letters A, B, C, and D and another group of the letters E, F, G, and H.

The structures of the four nucleotides which are formed by the breakdown of different kinds of RNA are shown in Fig. 10. It is seen that they all contain the sugar ribose, and all have a residue of phosphoric acid attached to carbon No. 5 of this ribose. They differ in the residue which is attached to carbon No. 1. This can be one of four closely related organic compounds called bases because they contain basic nitrogen atoms. Their names are adenine, guanine, cytosine, and uracil. (A few unusual kinds of RNA also give bases of slightly different structure.) In the nucleic acid, the four kinds of nucleotide are linked as shown in Fig. 11, on page 22. The simplest way to visualize the resulting molecule is as a chain made up of alternating residues of ribose and phosphoric acid, to carbon No. 1 of each ribose is linked a residue of one of the four bases.

The four nucleotides which are normally formed from DNA closely resemble those from RNA, but differ in the fact that the sugar has no oxygen atom on carbon No. 2, and, therefore, is called 2-deoxyribose. They also differ in the fact that one of the four bases is different; uracil is not found in DNA, but a closely related base, thymine, is found instead. The structure of the nucleotide containing thymine is shown in Fig. 12. (DNA, from a few organisms, also yields nucleotides in which cytosine has a methyl or hydroxymethyl group on its carbon No. 5.) In DNA, the nucleotides are linked together as they are in RNA. DNA molecules are best visualized as chains of alternating residues of deoxyribose and phosphoric acid, while to carbon No. 1 of each deoxyribose is normally linked one of the four bases.

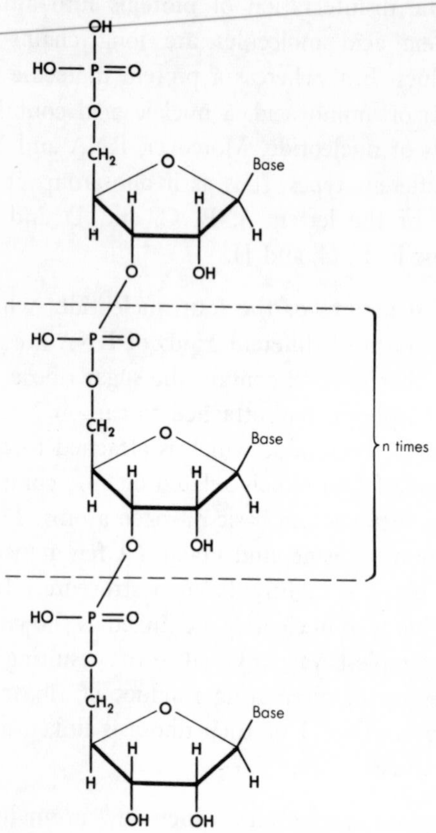

Fig. 11 The structure of RNA.

DNA and RNA molecules consist of single nucleotide chains—two or more chains are not linked in the way that two or more peptide chains are in many protein molecules. (The very important fact that DNA molecules are normally held in pairs by weak bonds, called hydrogen bonds, will be seen in a later chapter.) It is clear that one DNA or RNA molecule can differ from another in the length and spelling of its nucleotide chain. At first sight, it might seem that because there are only four kinds of nucleotide in DNA and RNA the number of possible molecules of each would be severely limited. This is

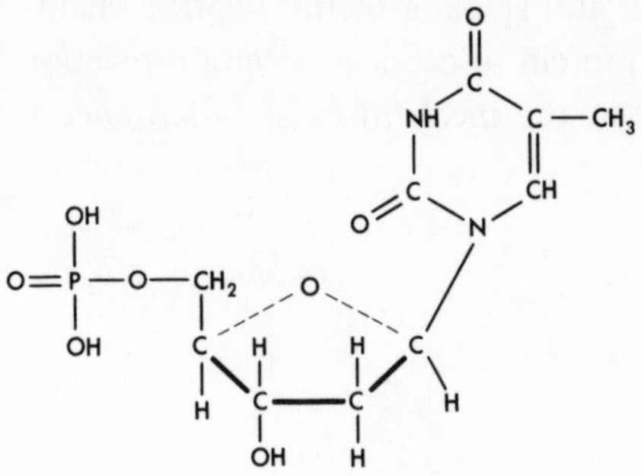

Fig. 12   Thymidylic acid, one of the four nucleotides of DNA.

not so: many billion different chains of 100 nucleotides could
be built up from four kinds of nucleotide. No methods have been
developed by which the complete spelling of a DNA or RNA
molecule can be found. But it is clear, as it is with amino acids in
a peptide chain, that each nucleotide is not repeated along the
chain at constant intervals. More details of the structure of different kinds of DNA and RNA will be given in later chapters.

7   CONCERNING ENZYMES

Hundreds of chemical reactions are continually proceeding within
living cells. Many of these are steps in the breakdown of food
molecules with the liberation of energy, while many others are
steps in the synthesis of proteins, nucleic acids, and other compounds of which the cell structure is made. Without catalysis,
most of these reactions would not occur at appreciable speeds.
The reason why they do occur is that almost every one of the
hundreds of reactions in a cell has its specific catalyst; these
catalysts are called enzymes, and all that have been isolated are
proteins.

It was seen that one protein differs from another in the length
and spelling of its peptide chain or chains. Hence, a certain

length and spelling of the peptide chains must confer the ability on a protein to catalyze a certain reaction. That is a fundamental point in the mechanism of inheritance to which we shall return later.

Structures
Within Cells
and Their
Component
Molecules

2

1 OUR INCREASING POWERS OF VISION

We have considered the structure of protein and nucleic acid
molecules on which, as will be seen later, inherited differences
between living organisms are founded. Our knowledge of these
molecules is the climax of over a century of work by chemists,
who first revealed the structure of the small and simple molecules of living organisms, and then, gradually, of the more and
more complex. Parallel with these chemical studies of molecules

of gradually increasing size has run the discovery by biologists of cell structures of gradually diminishing size. The microscopes available around the middle of the nineteenth century revealed that living cells, although of many shapes and sizes, are built on a common plan. In the center of most cells is a spherical object, the nucleus, and filling the remainder of the cell is a viscous fluid, the cytoplasm. As the years passed, light microscopes of increasing magnification were made, and techniques of revealing cell structures by staining were refined. As a result, the cytoplasm was seen to contain numerous particles. But the smallest cell particle discerned with the light microscope was enormous compared with the largest cell molecule whose structure has been discovered by the chemist. Between the two lay the mysterious, viscous fluid of the cytoplasm in which other particles could be dimly discerned.

Moreover, it could be proved that the size of the waves of visible light is too great for light microscopes ever to reveal the fine structure of the cytoplasm. Having struck this evidently impenetrable barrier, some biologists came to view the cytoplasm almost mystically. To it were attributed such qualities as "irritability" and "self-perpetuation," as though it contained in some subtle form the vital spirit of life. The names "cytoplasm" and "protoplasm" did not help, since they suggested entities which were mysteriously more than the atoms and molecules of which they were composed. These vague vitalist feelings permeated somewhat throughout biology, tending to inhibit clear thinking about the mechanism of living cells.

However, in the last few years the studies of chemists and microscopists have met: protein and nucleic acid molecules, whose structures are being discovered by the chemist, can now be seen in the electron microscope, which has about 1,000 times the resolving power of the most powerful light microscope (Fig. 13); and the smallest particles which can now be seen in the cytoplasm are composed of only a few protein and nucleic acid molecules. When two groups of engineers, boring a tunnel from

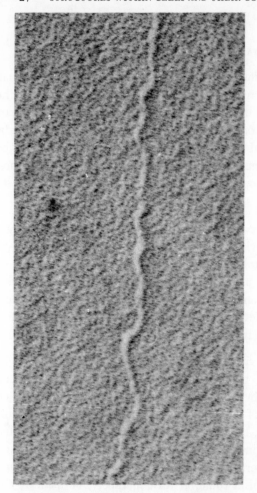

Fig. 13 Electron micrograph of part of a bonded pair of DNA molecules, magnification approximately 160,000 diameters. (Courtesy Dr. M. S. C. Birbeck.)

opposite sides of a mountain, finally crumble through the wall of rock that divides them, a shaft of light pierces the mountain. With this junction of chemists and microscopists, a shaft of light has, in effect, pierced the cell. The mist which shrouded the cytoplasm, and which evoked vague vitalist emotions, has been dispersed, and there remain no regions of the cell which are quite uncharted. In this chapter, the structures which can be seen within cells will be outlined, and the distribution among them of the proteins and nucleic acids of the cell will be described.

2 A DIGRESSION ON VITALISM

Although many vitalist beliefs have been vague and irrational, by no means all have been. Many clear minded scientists of the past, influenced by the complexity of living creatures, developed precise vitalist theories of a kind which could conceivably be put to experimental test. In this section a brief digression will be made to explain these theories, since they define important possibilities which should be borne in mind when attempting to explain biology in molecular terms.

To explain the theories of vitalists it is first necessary to state the theories with which they do not agree: those of mechanists. A mechanist believes that a living organism results from its component atoms and molecules being situated in the correct relative positions, and that life is solely the interaction of these atoms and molecules according to the same laws of chemistry and physics as are displayed in the inanimate world.

Those theories of vitalists which could conceivably be tested by experiment are of two distinct kinds. Those of the first kind can be illustrated by the ideas of Justus von Liebig, a great German biochemist of the nineteenth century. In his textbook, *Animal Chemistry*, he appears to agree with the mechanists that a living organism merely results from its component atoms and molecules being correctly situated relative to one another, and that a living organism could, at least in theory, be made in the laboratory. But he believed that when the atoms and molecules of a living organism are in their correct relative positions, a new force of nature manifests itself. This vital force is the principal cause of the molecular reactions and movements at the basis of life. This force, he believed, is inherent in all atoms and molecules but only manifests itself in the complex structure of the cell; and research in biochemistry would reveal the laws of its action, as experiments in physics had revealed the laws of gravitation and electrostatic attraction.

In contrast, vitalists of the second kind believe that the basis of life lies outside the normal realm of science. Their theories are varied, but the most clearly defined have been those of Hans Driesch who died in 1942. He started his career as an experimental biologist, and studied the development of fertilized eggs into adult organisms, and made important contributions to the subject, but he became convinced that this development would never be explained solely by the interaction of forces of nature of the kind normally investigated by scientists. As a result, he retired from experimental science early in this century, and became a professor of philosophy at the University of Heidelberg, where he developed his theories of vitalism.

Driesch believed that living organisms differ sharply from non-living in the possession of a vital force, and that this force is unlike those familiar to scientists. It is a purposive directive force of a kind suggested by Aristotle. Its purpose is that a living organism should grow to maturity and reproduce. It acts by directing the component parts of the organism into paths they would not take under the sole influence of the normal forces of nature, so causing the organism to develop and function correctly. Driesch claimed that the existence of this force was suggested by numerous characteristics of living organisms, such as the resistance of animals to infection, and was proved beyond all reasonable doubt by certain experiments in animal development. For example, when the fertilized egg of a sea-urchin begins to develop into the adult, it divides first into two cells, and these each divide into two more to give four. If allowed to continue development, each of these four cells will, by further division, give rise to different parts of the adult organism. But, if the four cells are broken apart and allowed to continue developing separately, they each give not different fragments of the adult, but a complete adult sea-urchin. Driesch concluded that the four cells are identical and that the normal forces of nature could not cause different parts of an adult to arise from each of four identical cells. Again, if the limbs of certain amphibia are removed, perfect new limbs develop in their place. Driesch considered that this could only come about under the influence of the directive vital force, which is attempting to resist damage to the organism, and could never occur if the component atoms and molecules of the animal were merely under the sway of the blind forces of nature of the inanimate world. The action of Driesch's vital force requires that the normal laws of nature can be violated in living organisms, and Driesch considered in detail how this violation might be detected. Whether a vital force of the kind postulated by Driesch could conceivably exist is open to philosophical argument. Whether, in fact, it does exist can be investigated by scientific experiment.

Both kinds of vitalist theory can be tested by trying to discover, as biochemists do, whether living organisms can be completely explained by the interaction of their component parts according to the normal laws of chemistry and physics. It will be seen in this book that the most fundamental processes of living cells, including their self-copying and inheritance, have recently been shown to be founded on the interaction of large molecules according to the normal laws of chemistry. No new force of nature appears necessary to explain these processes and, hence, a vital force of the kind suggested by Liebig does not seem to exist. But the fundamental processes of development, and the forces which cause the grouping of large molecules into cell structures, and the grouping of cells into organs, are not yet clearly understood. Therefore, a directive vital force of the kind suggested by Driesch cannot be excluded. Nevertheless, the recent spectacular discoveries in molecular biology have undermined the faith of biologists in vitalism of any kind; and evidence does, in fact, slowly accumulate against a vital force as suggested by Driesch.

In addition to vitalist theories about the basis of life, there are vitalist theories about the function of the brain. Again, the mechanist view is now dominant: that all manifestations of the brain, including the human brain, result from the interaction of its component parts according to the normal laws of chemistry and physics. But the problems here are far more complicated,

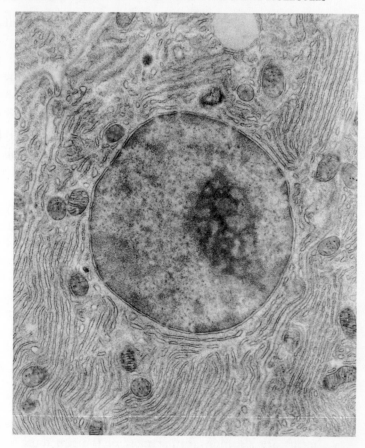

Fig. 14 Electron micrograph of section through the center of a cell from the pancreas of a bat, magnification approximately 10,000 diameters. (Courtesy Dr. D. W. Fawcett.)

and involve concepts such as consciousness and free will which are difficult to think clearly about, let alone investigate experimentally.

3 CELL STRUCTURES REVEALED BY THE ELECTRON MICROSCOPE

In Fig. 14 is shown an electron micrograph of a very fine slice of pancreas cell. In the center is the nucleus and outside it is the cytoplasm. It seems clear that the cytoplasm has a complicated structure and that both it, and the nucleus, contain thousands of tiny particles. In this section, two important points will be considered. How can we be sure that the structures we see in pictures of this kind are really present in the living cell, and how can we be sure that in the clear spaces between the smallest particles do not lie other important structures which are beyond the power of the electron microscope to reveal?

Before viewing in the electron microscope, cells must be killed by being treated rather violently with certain chemicals—a process known as fixing. They are often treated with a compound of the metal osmium, then dried and sliced very thinly. The osmium atoms have varying affinities for different structures in the cell, and become attached to them to different extents. The resulting electron micrographs are largely pictures of the distribution of osmium in the cell slice, since the cell structures themselves have little effect on the electron beam. Do the structures seen in such pictures all exist in the living cell, or are they partly spurious patterns produced by the harsh treatment?

The problem is by no means a new one in microscopy. For many years, fixation and staining have been used to reveal cell structures in the light microscope and the question has repeatedly arisen as to whether some of these are artifacts produced by the treatment. In these instances, numerous experiments have proved that staining has very largely revealed true cell structures. Experiments are also proving that most of the structures seen in the electron microscope are genuine cell components. For example, tiny particles can be isolated, by methods which will be described, from the cytoplasm of cells which have not been fixed. Their size and shape, as measured in the ultracentrifuge, are those of the smallest particles which can be seen in the cytoplasm of cells under the electron microscope.

These particles (which can just be seen in the cytoplasm of the cell in Fig. 14) have been named ribosomes, for reasons which will become apparent later. We now come to the second question. How can we be sure that in the clear spaces between the ribosomes do not lie other important structures which the electron microscope is unable to reveal? The answer comes first from experiments which show that each ribosome has about four million times the weight of a hydrogen atom. This can be roughly calculated from their size in electron micrographs, and calculated more accurately from their speed of sedimentation in the ultracentrifuge. A medium-sized protein or nucleic acid molecule has a molecular weight of around 40,000, hence a ribosome could contain only around one hundred of these molecules. Therefore, any particles in the cytoplasm, invisible in the electron microscope, must have considerably less than one hundred times the size of an average protein or nucleic acid molecule. Second, when cell particles are isolated by centrifuging broken cells, in a manner that will soon be described, it can be shown clearly that structures in the cytoplasm smaller than ribosomes are, in fact, individual molecules.

An electron micrograph, such as that in Fig. 14, therefore, reveals the smallest organized structures of a cell. It will be seen in later chapters that the basis of inheritance lies in the interaction of large molecules with these structures. This is to be expected. If we tried to discover how a cell functions by studying its small molecules, we would have reached too simple a level of organization—like a man who tried to discover how a car works by making a chemical analysis of its valves and pistons. An important point follows from this fact. Very small objects, of the size of an electron, do not behave like the solid objects around us in everyday life, but as a strange mixture of solid object and wave; and the laws of nature prevent us from ever gaining enough precise information about them to predict accurately their future behavior. Actually, these properties are possessed to an infinitesimal degree by the objects of everyday life, but they have no practical importance. Neither have they any practical importance with objects the size of protein and nucleic acid molecules, and hence these properties need not be considered in explaining the basis of inheritance.

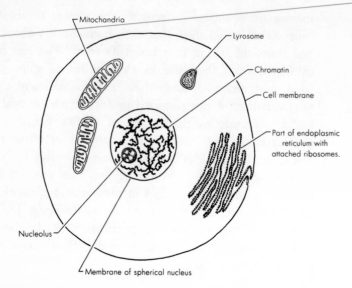

Fig. 15   Diagram of typical animal cell as seen under the electron microscope.

4   A SUMMARY OF THE STRUCTURES FOUND IN CELLS

Many kinds of cells have been viewed under the electron microscope and, although they vary in size and shape, it is quite clear
that they have many structures in common. The structures which,
it has been concluded, exist in a "typical" animal cell are shown
in the diagram of Fig. 15. In the center is the large, roughly
spherical, nucleus. The nucleus is bounded by a membrane, and
the bulk of the material within it appears as a mass of coarse
particles. The particles within the nucleus have been given the
noncommittal name of chromatin because they are readily stained
with certain dyes, and can then also be clearly seen in the light
microscope. Also, within the nucleus lies one small sphere, or a few
small spheres, called the nucleoli. They also contain granules. The
nucleus has this appearance during most of the life of the cell,
but before cell division it changes radically, as will be described
later.

The largest structures normally found outside the nucleus, in the cytoplasm, are the mitochondria, which are shown in the diagram of Fig. 15. They have a fairly complicated internal structure and are important, but we shall not be concerned with them in this book. They contain enzymes whose function is to oxidize acetic acid, which is produced from more complex compounds, to carbon dioxide and water, with the production of energy. Thus, they are power units and are found in large numbers in cells that need large amounts of energy, such as muscle cells. Bacteria do not have mitochondria, but they usually perform the same chemical reactions, with similar enzymes differently arranged. Plant cells contain mitochondria, and, in addition, often contain chloroplasts which are of similar size and somewhat related structure. Their function is to absorb light energy, and store it in compounds that provide chemical energy to the plant. Other particles found in the cytoplasm which need not concern us are centrosomes, involved in cell division, and lysosomes

Fig. 16   Electron micrograph of endoplasmic reticulum showing attached ribosomes, magnification 30,000 diameters. (Courtesy Dr. D. W. Facett.)

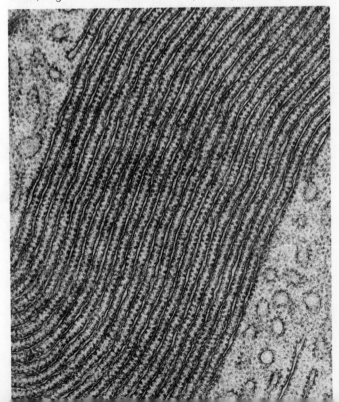

which are capsules containing enzymes which catalyze the break-down of the contents of the cell.

Throughout the remainder of the cytoplasm of most cells, other than bacteria, a system of membranes branches out, which has been named the endoplasmic reticulum, Fig. 16. The three-dimensional structure of the reticulum is difficult to deduce from electron micrographs. The membranes always appear in pairs with a narrow gap between them, and by some microscopists it is concluded that these gaps are part of a system of interconnecting canals, which join with the outside of the cell through holes in the cell membrane—somewhat like woodworm tunnels in a rotten wooden ball. On the surfaces of the membranes of the endoplasmic reticulum away from the gaps between them, the tiny particles named ribosomes are always scattered. They are most plentiful in cells which are rapidly forming proteins, such as the cells of the pancreas which make digestive enzymes. Certain cells, including bacteria, have no endoplasmic reticulum, but they do have ribosomes, and these appear to be freely distributed through the cytoplasm.

Fig. 17 Photograph of dividing cell of onion root showing chromosomes. (Copyright by General Biological Supply House, Inc., Chicago.)

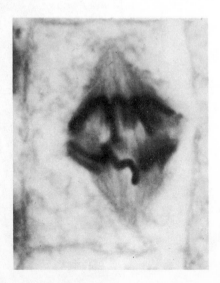

Just before cell division, the appearance of the nucleus changes completely. The nucleoli and nuclear membrane disappear, and the particles of chromatin become concentrated into a number of threadlike objects called chromosomes (Fig. 17). It has been proved that the chromosomes still remain intact even between cell divisions when they are invisible. The particles of chromatin, which then appear to be separate from one another, still in fact form part of the chromosomes which have become finely drawn out.

In a higher animal or plant the number of chromosomes is the same in nearly every cell, and is typical of the species. The cells of a man, for example, generally contain forty-six chromosomes, though occasionally tissue cells are found which contain twice or three times this number. The most important variation from the normal number of chromosomes per cell is found in egg cells, and sperm or pollen cells, which contain exactly half. At fertilization, when an egg and sperm cell unite, the normal number is restored.

Since most cells of an organism contain the same number of chromosomes, it is clear that, at cell division, the number of chromosomes must normally double. This doubling can be observed microscopically. Each chromosome appears to divide lengthways and the two halves separate into different cells. It is also clear that, in a division which precedes the formation of egg and sperm cells, the chromosomes of the parent cell must be portioned equally between the daughter cells without any increase in their number. In man, for example, the forty-six chromosomes of the parent cell must be divided into two groups of twenty-three. Such a process of "meiosis" can be seen under the microscope during the formation of germ cells. An important observation is that the chromosomes are not divided at random into the two groups. The chromosomes can be seen to vary in shape and size, but there are two of each shape and size. During meiosis these come to lie in pairs, side by side. The members of each pair then divide lengthways and the resulting four chromosomes separate, after two cell divisions, into four separate nuclei.

(For a more detailed account see Selected Readings, p. 133.) The cells of lower organisms also contain chromosomes as will be seen later.

5 THE ISOLATION OF CELL STRUCTURES

The electron microscope reveals many structures in cells, but gives little clue as to what they are made of. The most direct way to find this is to isolate and analyze each kind of structure. For many years biochemists tried to do this by grinding up cells in salt solutions, and centrifuging the resulting suspension first at low and then at high speeds. They hoped that first the larger and then the smaller particles would sediment. But they could see, by examining the various sediments under the microscope, that they were getting no clear-cut isolation of the different cell structures. Then, in the 1940's it was discovered that the reason for this failure was that many of the cell structures burst when they entered the salt solution, and that this bursting could be prevented by substituting a solution of cane sugar. Successful methods of isolating cell structures were then soon developed.

The methods that are used will be illustrated by describing a particular isolation. Suppose we wanted to isolate various structures from the cells of liver. The procedure, like many scientific operations, does not require extreme skill. We would first prepare, and cool in a refrigerator, a cane sugar solution of the strength recommended in the biochemical recipe book, from which we were taking details of the operation. If we decided to use rat's liver, we would kill a rat and rapidly dissect out its liver. Then we would weigh out a few grams of it and drop it into the recommended volume of the ice cold sugar solution. Next, in a refrigerated room, we would disintegrate the liver in a blender. One kind is the device with a rapidly rotating steel blade which originated in the laboratory, but has become a standard kitchen liquidizer. The rotating blade sets up shearing forces in the liquid which tear the cells apart and liberate their contents.

We would then put the resulting suspension in a small centrifuge tube, and centrifuge it in a refrigerated centrifuge. By spinning the tube for ten minutes at a slow speed which will exert 700 times the force of gravity on the suspended particles, we would get a sediment which is largely cell nuclei, but also contains unbroken cells and fragments of cells. To get purer nuclei we would pour off the liquid from above the sediment, and resuspend it in more sugar solution, and centrifuge once more.

The liquid we first poured off from above the sedimented nuclei contains the smaller cell structures. If we spin this in another tube at a speed which exerts 5,000 times the force of gravity, the sediment which forms is largely mitochondria. They can again be purified by recentrifuging. To isolate smaller cell structures it is necessary to use a preparative ultracentrifuge. This is no larger than other preparative centrifuges but is made with great precision and is expensive. It can rotate plastic tubes at up to 40,000 revolutions per minute, and the tubes are spun in a vacuum to prevent heat being generated by friction.

If we spun the liquid remaining from the isolation of the mitochondria for one hour at a speed which gives 100,000 times the force of gravity, we would obtain a sediment of particles which, a few years ago, were named microsomes. This name is unfortunate, for the electron microscope has since shown that these are fragments of the endoplasmic reticulum, and not worthy of a special name. Attached to their surfaces can be seen ribosomes, and it has been found that if they are stirred with a solution of a detergent, the endoplasmic reticulum dissolves, leaving a suspension of ribosomes. These can then be isolated by spinning once more at 100,000 times the force of gravity. No matter how long we centrifuge, no more particles sediment out of the liquid which remains after separating the microsomes. In an analytical ultracentrifuge it can be seen that, at 100,000 times the force of gravity, individual protein and nucleic acid molecules begin to migrate through this liquid, and that it contains no larger particles. Hence, the cells contain no structures smaller than ribosomes—proof of the point which was discussed in an earlier section.

6 THE PROTEIN AND NUCLEIC ACID CONTENT OF CELL STRUCTURES

If we isolate cell structures by the methods described in the last section, we find that the nuclei, mitochondria and ribosomes, and also the "supernatant" fraction which remains when these have been removed, all contain a substantial proportion of proteins. Apart from water, proteins make up quite the largest part of the mitochondria and supernatant fraction, and it is probable that virtually all their proteins are enzymes. The greater part of the non-aqueous portion of nuclei is also composed of proteins. These are partly enzymes, but partly peculiar proteins called histones which are small molecules containing a high proportion of amino acids with basic side chains. Chromosomes can be isolated from nuclei by a method that will be described in a later chapter, and are found to consist of up to fifty per cent of histones, and to contain all the histones of the nucleus. Proteins make up about forty-five per cent of the dry weight of ribosomes. How many kinds of protein molecule are present is not yet clear, and no enzymes have been found among them.

RNA is also widely distributed through the cell. Ribosomes, as their name denotes, contain a high percentage (about fifty-five per cent of their weight), hence they are composed solely of RNA and protein. As a result, a large part of the RNA of a cell is concentrated in the ribosomes. In liver cells, ribosomes contain about one-half of the total RNA. Nuclei and the supernatant fraction contain only a small percentage of RNA. Most of the RNA of the nuclei is concentrated in the nucleoli, while in the supernatant, the RNA consists of individual molecules in solution. Although the percentage of RNA in these fractions is low, because they make up a large proportion of the total weight of the cell, they contain a fairly large proportion of the cell's

RNA. About twelve per cent of the RNA of liver cells is contained in the nuclei, and about thirty-four per cent in the supernatant fraction. Mitochrondria contain only a small percentage of RNA and only a small proportion of the RNA of the cell. The important concentrations of RNA within cells are, therefore, in the ribosomes, in the nuclei, and in the water of the cytoplasm. It will be seen later that RNA in each of these three places plays an important role in molecular biology.

When animal cell fractions are analyzed for DNA, it is found to be absent from every cell structure except the nucleus. It can also be shown, by staining cells with stains that react only with DNA, that it is also absent from every part of the nucleus except the chromatin of a resting cell, and the chromosomes of a dividing cell. If chromosomes are isolated, by the method to be described later, they are found to contain up to forty per cent DNA. Plant cells also seem to have traces of DNA in the chloroplasts.

7   THE DNA CONTENT OF VARIOUS CELLS

It was seen in the last section that DNA has a remarkably restricted distribution in cells. There is another peculiarity that marks DNA off from the other components of living organisms, which is revealed by measuring the total quantity of DNA in different cells. Suppose we want to determine the quantity of DNA per cell in different tissues of a hen. One way to go about this is to kill a hen, and isolate samples of nuclei from its liver, kidney, spleen, and other tissues. These are suspended in a solution of cane sugar. A known fraction of the suspension is then taken, and its DNA content is determined, and the number of nuclei in another known fraction is counted under the microscope. It is then possible to calculate the average quantity of DNA per nucleus, hence per cell, from which the nuclei came. This experiment has been done, and the results published. The average quantities of DNA per liver, kidney, and spleen cell of the hen were found to be 2.6, 2.3, and 2.6×10^{-12} gm respectively. The amount in a red blood cell of the hen was also determined on a suspension of these cells and found to be 2.6 × 10⁻¹² gm. Values very close to these have been found on other domestic fowls, and it appears that the average quantity of DNA per cell is, at least very nearly, constant. To this rule an important exception was discovered. The average amount of DNA per cell in a suspension of sperm cells from a cockerel has been found to be 1.3×10^{-12} gm, or just half the quantity in other body cells. Similar experiments have been done on other species. Again, the quantity of DNA per body cell is very nearly constant in any one species, but differs between species, and again the sperm cells contain one half of the DNA in tissue cells. For example, the tissue cells of a cow or steer all contain very nearly 6.0×10^{-12} gm of DNA per cell, while the sperms of a bull contain 3.0×10^{-12} gm.

These methods determine the average quantity of DNA per cell in a sample of cells. With an apparatus known as a quantitative cytophotometer, it is possible to measure the quantity of DNA in a single cell. In this apparatus, a section of a tissue, or a smear of separate cells, is placed on the slide of a special quartz microscope, and a beam of ultraviolet light is focused onto the nucleus of a single cell. The light which passes through the nucleus is allowed to fall on a photoelectric cell, and its intensity is compared with that of a similar beam which has merely passed through the quartz slide. The difference in intensity depends on the quantity of DNA in the nucleus, which can be calculated. This method again shows that the quantity of DNA in every single cell of any one species is at least very nearly the same, with a few exceptions. These exceptions are that the sperm cells, and also the egg cells, contain half the quantity in normal cells, and that tissue cells which have two or three times the normal number of chromosomes, contain two or three times the normal amount of DNA. From all these facts an important conclusion may be drawn, the significance of which will appear later. It is that for a single species, a complete set of chromosomes always contains the same quantity of DNA.

Genes:
Structures
Within Cells
That Control
Heredity

3

1 GREGOR MENDEL

Heredity is the tendency of like to beget like, a tendency shown by all living things, but most clearly by single-celled organisms. When, for example, an *E. coli* bacterium, or an amoeba, divides to give two progeny, these have identical, or almost identical, appearance and properties to the parent. Why is this so? At first sight the answer might seem obvious: because at cell division the component molecules and larger structures of the cell tend to be distributed evenly between the two daughter cells. But this explanation is inadequate because, on the average, the daughter cells are half the parental size, and must double in size before they in turn divide. It is this doubling that is the basic problem of heredity. Since cells are made of molecules, it must normally involve a doubling in the number of each kind of molecule in the cell. It is possible to conceive of various ways in which this process might come about, but all involve some form of self-copying by certain molecules of cells. There might conceivably be only one kind of molecule in the cell, which could form copies of itself, and this might direct the formation, or entry into the cell, of all other molecules. Or there might be many kinds of molecules which could form self-copies. Or one kind of molecule might catalyze the copying of another, which in turn catalyzed the copying of the first.

The first clues to the correct answer to this problem came, not from studies of cell molecules or the division of single-celled organisms, but from Mendel's experiments in the last century on inheritance in pea plants. Heredity in such higher organisms is less obviously related to the replication of cell molecules than it is in single-celled organisms. It is, nevertheless, founded on it as we can nowadays understand. For example, flower color in peas, which Mendel studied, results from cells of the flower forming molecules of a certain pigment. This pigment was not present in the pollen or egg cell which united to give the fertilized egg from which the flowers were derived. But the pigment must have been formed by some molecule, or molecules, which were present in the pollen or egg cell (or both), and which were exactly copied after each cell division.

Mendel was the unwitting founder of molecular biology, and the outline of his life is well known. He was born in 1822, the son of a farmer, and at twenty-one became an Augustinian monk. He lived for most of his life at the Altbrünn Monastery in Brünn, which was then in the Austrian Empire. In the monastery garden he carried out his experiments on inheritance in peas which were published in the Brünn scientific journal, but their significance was not grasped until after his death.

But this familiar outline tends to romanticize Mendel's life, and to provide no clear explanation of his scientific ability. In fact, he was not a monk in the sense of being a member of a large enclosed community. His monastery contained only about thirteen priests who were chosen for their intellectual ability. They were

Fig. 18   Mendel and his fellow monks. He is standing one from the extreme right. (Courtesy of Mrs. Anne Iltis.)

free to travel and receive guests, and the monastery was an important intellectual center with an excellent cuisine. Figure 18 shows Mendel, at the time of his experiments, with his fellow monks. The abbot, in the front row, was an oriental scholar of repute, and also included are a famous authority on Goethe, and a noted composer and expert on church music. Mendel entered the monastery with a good education, and was then sent to the

University of Vienna for two years to study science. After his return, he taught biology for fourteen years at a secular high school in the town, with an excellent staff and over a thousand boys. Reminiscences of his pupils show that he was a friendly humorous man and a good teacher. It was during this period that Mendel performed his experiments. He was later elected abbot of his monastery. It is clearly no more remarkable that Mendel should have performed successful experiments in his monastery garden, than that Darwin should have done so in the garden of his home near London.

It is an amusing pastime (though not one to be indulged in too seriously) to classify scientists into two groups. The first is a tiny group of creators whose interests range wide, and who show us new ways of looking at the facts of nature. Darwin did this when he organized what were, largely, known facts into overwhelming evidence that species have arisen by evolution. The second is a vast group of craftsmen and technicians, more or less skilled at uncovering the mechanism of a limited portion of nature with the scientific method as their tool (a tool which was originally forged by the creators). Mendel, like most great scientists, seems to fall into the second group as a supreme craftsman. He made a brilliant study of an important, but limited, part of nature, and he devised a lucid theory to explain his results.

2 MENDEL'S THEORY OF INHERITANCE

The phenomenon of heredity is an obvious fact of life, but before Mendel announced the results of his experiments no satisfactory explanation of it had been given. A popular theory was that both a father and a mother contributed to their offspring some kind of fluid which contained an essence of their characteristics. The blend of the two fluids determined the characteristics of the off-spring, which tended to be intermediate between those of the two parents. The fluids were thought to be related in some way to blood, and from this idea originated such expressions as, "a little Irish blood in his veins." But a number of facts did not fit with this theory and it was not generally accepted by scientists. For example, if a black sheep is crossed with a white ram their offspring are not grey but pure white; and if these breed amongst themselves some of their offspring will be white and some black.

In the early nineteenth century numerous experiments had been performed on plant hybridization—the crossing of plants which differ from one another. But, as Mendel pointed out at the beginning of his paper, there had been "formulated no generally applicable law governing the formation and development of hybrids." He added, "Those who survey the work done in this department will arrive at the conviction that among all the numerous experiments made, not one has been carried out to such an extent and in such a way as to make it possible to determine the number of different forms under which the offspring of hybrids appear, or to arrange these forms with certainty according to their separate generations, or to definitely ascertain their statistical relations." This he intended to remedy. His paper describes a precise and elegant series of experiments on hybridization in peas and advances a simple theory to explain the results. He implies that his theory could explain the facts of heredity in general.

Mendel's theory of heredity will be explained first, and the experiments from which he derived it will be described later. The theory is really made up of two parts: a theory of precisely how one plant differs from the next in its inherited character, and a theory of how this character originates in each plant. The first part suggests that the general character that any plea plant inherits can be subdivided into a large but limited number of characteristics which, in this book, will be called "unit characters." Flower color is an example of a unit character. Plants which differ in their inherited character do so in possessing one or more of these unit characters in sharply different forms. One plant, for example, can have red flowers and another white. This revolutionary theory suggested how a precise analysis could be made of differences in character which had previously been considered only in a general and descriptive way.

We now know that Mendel's theory that an individual is a mosaic of unit characters is correct. It extends to all living organisms and is one of the basic principles of biology. It implies that the possible number of genetically different individuals in a species, though large, is limited. For example, genetically different human beings result from the alternative forms of the thousands of unit characters being combined together in different ways. If all these ways were exhausted, any further individuals would be identical twins of those that had come before. The theory, in effect, claims that inherited character is built up from a number of fundamental particles. If heredity is to be explained in chemical terms, this is a necessary consequence of the particulate theory of matter.

The second part of Mendel's theory explains how the particular form in which each unit character will appear is determined. He suggested, in effect although not in so many words, that every egg and pollen cell of the pea plant carries one determinant for each unit character. The fertilized egg therefore carries two determinants for each character, and the form in which the character will appear is decided by their interaction. For example, every egg and pollen cell carries a determinant for flower color. If both cells which combine to form the fertilized egg carry the determinant for red, the flowers will be red, and if for white, the flowers will be white. If one cell carries the determinant for red and the other carries that for white, the flowers, as will be seen later, will be red. Mendel did not consider the nature of the determinants. After the rediscovery of his work, it was suggested by some biologists that they had no reality, but were merely convenient figments for explaining the facts of heredity. The suggestion parallels another made in the nineteenth century that atoms and molecules have no physical reality. It is now clear that Mendel's determinants, which have been named genes, have as real an existence as do atoms and molecules, and that they control the appearance of unit characters in all living organisms.

3   MENDEL'S EVIDENCE IN SUPPORT OF HIS THEORY

Chemists of the eighteenth century discovered that matter is composed of particles largely because they made precise measurements of the quantities of compounds that react together, rather than merely describing the appearances of chemical reactions. Similarly, Mendel discovered the particulate nature of inheritance largely because he made precise counts of the number of plants which showed different characters, rather than merely describing them as his predecessors had done. Mendel chose pea plants for his experiments for two reasons: because they possess sharp differences in numerous points of character, and because their flowers are normally self-fertilized, and receive no pollen from without unless this is introduced experimentally. He selected strains of plants which differed sharply in one or more of seven characteristics, and which maintained these differences through generations of self-fertilization. The seven characteristics are examples of what we shall call the unit characters of his theory. Their alternative forms were round or wrinkled seed, yellow or green seed, red or white flowers, smooth or wrinkled pods, green or yellow pods, flowers distributed along the stem or bunched at the end, and stems of six to seven feet or of three quarters to one and a half feet.

He first made crosses between these plants to produce hybrid seed. He found that when the parent plants differed in a certain unit character, one of the alternative forms always appeared in the hybrid to the exclusion of the other. For example, when the pollen from round seeded plants was used to fertilize the flowers of wrinkled seeded plants, or vice versa, the seeds which formed from these flowers were always round. Or, when red flowered plants were crossed with white flowered ones, and the seeds which formed were grown into new plants, these plants all had red flowers. Mendel called round seed, and red flowers, the "dominant" forms of these two unit characters. The dominant forms of the other characters were yellow seed, smooth pods, green pods, flowers along the stem, and stems of over six feet.

Mendel then grew large numbers of each of these seven kinds of hybrid seed into plants which he allowed to self-fertilize, and he then collected the seeds which formed. Some of these seeds, or the plants which were grown from them, showed the forms of the unit characters which had disappeared in their parents. For example, Mendel grew 253 hybrid round seeded plants and allowed them to self-fertilize. In the pods, which formed on the plants, were usually both round and wrinkled seeds. The wrinkled form of the character had obviously been latent in the hybrid plant, and he called it the "recessive" form of the character.

Findings of this kind—the disappearance of a characteristic in a cross and its reappearance in subsequent generations—had been observed by plant breeders before Mendel. His important discovery resulted from counting the numbers of different forms of each character. This revealed remarkably simple ratios between them. For example, from the hybrid round seeded plants which had been allowed to self-fertilize he collected 7,324 seeds; 5,474 were round and 1,850 were wrinkled, a ratio of 2.96 to 1. From large numbers of each of the six other kinds of hybrid plants he obtained, after self-fertilization, the dominant and recessive forms in the ratios of 3.01, 3.15, 2.95, 2.82 and 3.14 to 1. All these ratios, as Mendel perceived, are nearly 3 to 1, and they approached nearest to it when large numbers of plants were counted.

This ratio provides beautiful evidence of the truth of Mendel's theories which were discussed in the last section. He implied that every egg and pollen cell contains one determinant for each unit character, and the fertilized egg, therefore, contains two. In a hybrid fertilized egg the determinants for at least one unit character will differ. When the resulting hybrid plant forms egg cells or pollen cells, one half will contain the determinant for one form of this character, and the other half will contain that for the other. For example, half of both the pollen and egg cells from the hybrid round seeded plants will contain the determinant for round seed and half that for wrinkled. When these cells fertilize one another "it remains," in Mendel's words, "purely a matter of chance which of the two sorts of pollen will become united with each separate egg cell." It is like the simultaneous tossing of two coins: there is one chance that two heads will fall together, to two chances that a head will fall with a tail, to one chance that two tails with fall together. Hence, after a large number of self-fertilizations, one quarter of the eggs will contain two determinants for round seed, one quarter will contain two for wrinkled, and one half will contain one for each. Only the eggs which contain two determinants for wrinkled seed will in fact become wrinkled seed, and hence there will be a ratio of 3 to 1 between round and wrinkled seed. The round seeds should be of two kinds. When grown into plants, one-third should, on self-fertilization, give only round seed, while two-thirds should give round and wrinkled in the ratio of 3 to 1. Mendel tested these round seeds and proved that this was in fact so.

Mendel also performed experiments to test another point: in effect, whether the determinants for different unit characters are linked together in any way. For example, he had two strains of plants which had always bred true and which differed in two unit characters. One gave seeds which were both round and yellow, and the other gave seeds which were both wrinkled and green. Were the determinants for round and yellow seed, and those for wrinkled and green seed, linked together or could they separate freely? To discover the answer he crossed plants of the two strains together and, as expected, the resulting seeds were all round and yellow. He grew these seeds into plants and allowed them to self-fertilize. He had proved that half the pollen and egg cells from these plants contain the round determinant, and half the wrinkled; also, that half contain the yellow determinant and half the green. Did those cells that contained the round determinant contain only the yellow, because these two determinants were linked together, or did half contain the yellow and half the green? If the two pairs of determinants were in fact linked, this self fertilization would give only round, yellow seeds and wrinkled, green seeds, in the ratio of 3 to 1. Mendel in fact found all four combinations, often in the same pod. Out of 556 seeds, 315 were round and yellow, 101 wrinkled and yellow, 108 round and green, and thirty-two wrinkled and green. The ratio between these is 9.8 to 3.2 to 3.4 to 1. If the determinants for the two characters separated quite independently the ratio should be 9 to 3 to 3 to 1. Mendel concluded from this, and similar experiments, that they do move independently, and that deviations between the experimental and theoretical ratios were due to chance.

Mendel also performed other comprehensive experiments which strongly support his theories. When reading his paper it is painful to think of the unrewarded emotional energy which must have gone into his experiments on peas, which took him seven years to complete. It is not surprising that in his later years he seems to have had a mild persecution complex.

4   MENDEL'S PAIRED DETERMINANTS SHOWN TO LIE ON PAIRED CHROMOSOMES

If Mendel's determinants really exist, where do they lie in the germ cells; and do they also occur in all other cells of an organism? Mendel did not pursue these questions and they were not considered until his work was rediscovered eighteen years after his death. The reason why the significance of his work was not grasped immediately is difficult to decide. His paper was read by a number of leading biologists (though apparently not by Darwin) and it was quoted in books on hybridization. Although he was politely commended for his thorough techniques, nobody grasped what he was driving at. Part of the reason is probably that his experiments and theory, though extremely lucid, are somewhat shrouded in modest and abstract language. Also, he tended to express himself in mathematics, which most biologists are not quick to grasp. For example, he summarizes his experiments which show that determinants for different characters are not linked by saying, "the offspring of the hybrids in which several essentially different characters are combined represent the terms of a series of combinations, in which the developmental series for each pair of differentiating characters are associated." This is preceded by an algebraic expression occupying five lines. Above all, it is probable that his thinking was unfashionable, and that, in their initial enthusiasm for evolution by natural selection, biologists were unsympathetic to a theory which suggested that new individuals could arise solely by the reassortment of the fixed characters of their parents. However convincing Mendel's numerical ratios may have appeared, most biologists probably dismissed them because they could not be integrated into contemporary theories. Apparently strong evidence for precognition and extrasensory perception is dismissed today because it appears incongruous, and hence is justifiably suspected of hidden flaws.

By the end of the century, experimentation along Mendel's lines had become fashionable, for it was clear that biology could not advance far without a precise knowledge of the laws of inheritance. Around 1900, three biologists independently made similar discoveries to Mendel's, and after completing their experiments, discovered a reference to Mendel's work. A flood of experiments on inheritance followed, and rapid advances were made in a very few years. It was quickly perceived, as the reader may have done, that structures had already been discovered in cells which must almost certainly be the carriers of Mendel's determinants. These determinants must be present in pairs in the fertilized egg and possibly in many other cells. But when the germ cells are formed these determinants must separate, only one of each pair passing into a germ cell. The chromosomes are the cell structures that move in the way required of Mendel's determinants.

Normal cells contain an even number of chromosomes, while germ cells contain half this number. If a pair of Mendel's determinants are carried on the different members of a pair of chromosomes, the 3 to 1 ratio between the dominant and recessive forms of a unit character, when hybrid peas self-fertilize, is explained.

However, Mendel proved that the determinants of the different unit characters which he studied are not linked together. If this were a universal rule the number of determinants in any organism would be limited to the number of chromosomes. Now, the number of chromosomes in any cell is never large—germ cells of the pea plant, for example, each contain seven—and it was not possible that unit characters could be limited to this small number. It seemed clear that Mendel had chanced to study characters whose determinants lie on different members of the seven pairs of chromosomes, and that each chromosome carries many determinants which are in fact linked together. Experiments, done largely by T. H. Morgan and his colleagues at Columbia University, around 1910, showed that this was in fact so. By proving that the determinants in germ cells fall into linked groups, equal in number to that of the chromosomes, he gave conclusive evidence that the determinants do lie on the chromosomes, as will now be described.

Since the start of the twentieth century, Mendel's determinants have been named "genes" and this name will be used from now on. To continue genetic experiments where Mendel had left off, Morgan chose the fruit or vinegar fly, *Drosophila melanogaster*, because it breeds rapidly and is easy to look after. He bred large numbers of the flies in milk bottles, and in only a few months performed experiments similar to those that had taken Mendel some years. Morgan soon showed that Mendel's discoveries with pea plants applied to Drosophila. Thus, normal and vestigial wings appeared to be alternative forms of a single unit character, the appearance of which resulted from the interaction of a pair of genes. When normal flies were crossed with those with vestigial wings, their progeny were all normal. But, when these were crossed with one another, vestigial wings reappeared in their progeny, and the ratio between the dominant and recessive forms was 3 to 1.

Morgan, like Mendel, also proved that the genes for certain different unit characters were not linked together. Thus, when flies with smooth eyes and grey bodies were crossed with those with rough eyes and black bodies, their progeny had smooth eyes and grey bodies. But if these were crossed among themselves, the progeny contained flies with smooth eyes and black bodies and flies with rough eyes and grey bodies, as well as the two original combinations. The numbers of the four combinations were in the ratio of 9 to 3 to 3 to 1, which had been found by Mendel in similar experiments.

However, Morgan showed that many genes were not free to separate in this way. For example, when flies with normal wings and grey bodies were crossed with those with vestigial wings and black bodies, their progeny all had normal wings and grey bodies. If these were crossed with one another, only the two original combinations appeared in the progeny (with a few very important exceptions) and the ratio between the numbers of each was 3 to 1. Clearly, these genes controlling wing shape and body color are joined together in some way. Morgan studied the inheritance of hundreds of unit characters in *Drosophila melanogaster* and found that the genes controlling them fell into four pairs of linked groups. Normal cells of this fly contain four pairs of chromosomes. Other species of Drosophila have between three and six pairs of chromosomes, and they were shown to have an equal number of pairs of linked groups of genes. Experiments in the intervening years have confirmed beyond all possible doubt this strong evidence that the pairs of genes which control each unit character are carried on pairs of chromosomes.

5   THE ARRANGEMENT OF PAIRED GENES ON PAIRED CHROMOSOMES

It may be concluded that genes, the structures in cells which control heredity, are portions of chromosomes. Breeding experiments on the fruit fly, and other higher organisms, have provided one more clue which helps in discovering the chemical structure of genes. This clue is that genes are arranged one after another along the length of a chromosome—a conclusion which has followed from the discovery that linked genes do occasionally become separated.

For instance, it was seen in the last section that when fruit flies with normal wings and grey bodies are crossed with those with vestigial wings and black bodies, their progeny all have normal wings and grey bodies. If these flies are crossed with one another, almost all of their progeny resemble one or other of the two grandparents, because the genes controlling the two unit characters are linked. But a few flies in every hundred usually have normal wings and black bodies, and roughly the same number have vestigial wings and grey bodies. It is clear that the linkage between the two genes must occasionally break when the hybrid flies form germ cells. This occasional separation of linked genes is also found when the inheritance of other characters is studied. It suggests that pairs of chromosomes must occasionally break during the formation of germ cells, so separating certain linked genes. After the breakage, part of one chromosome must reunite with a different part of the other, so linking together genes which were originally on different chromosomes.

This process of chromosome breaking and reuniting can, in fact, be observed if the cell divisions which precede the formation of germ cells are studied under the microscope. It will be remembered that during meiosis the chromosomes pair, and the members of each pair divide to form a total of four chromosomes of similar shape and size which eventually separate into four different nuclei. Before this separation two of the four chromosomes, each derived from different parent chromosomes, can usually be seen to have formed one or more cross-shaped junctions or chiasmata. At each chiasma the chromosomes break, and the fragments from different chromosomes reunite. The chromosomes may form a chiasma at any point along their length, but this point is always the same distance from the same end of each chromosome. As a result, although the two new chromosomes which are formed are built up of segments of the original two, they are both of the original length. The process can be illustrated as follows. Suppose we had two chains each composed of twenty-six "plug in" necklace beads, which represent the two chromosomes. Suppose we mark the beads in one chain with the capital letters A to Z in the correct order, and in the other with the small letters *a* to *z*. Then we lay the chains straight out side by side, with the letters in the two chains correctly aligned. Then we break each chain at the same point and recombine the sections from different chains. Suppose the breakage had been between the letters *L* and *M* on one chain and *l* and *m* on the other. Then one of the new chains will have A to L in large, and *m* to *z* in small letters. The other will have *a* to *l* in small, and M to Z in large letters.

An important conclusion follows from the fact that "crossing over" occurs at any point along the length of the chromosomes. Suppose that the genes for two different unit characters were situated at opposite ends of each chromosome. Then the linkage between the genes for the two characters would be broken every time crossing over occurred. But, if one gene were situated at one extreme end of each chromosome, and the other at the middle, then, on the average, the linkage would be broken only half the times that crossing over occurred. While, if the two genes were at the same point the linkage between them would never be broken. Therefore, if different genes are situated at different points along the chromosomes, we would expect to find, in breeding experiments, that the frequency with which the linkage between different pairs of genes on a single chromosome is broken does vary. In the fruit fly and other organisms which have been studied, this variance is found, and from the different frequencies of separation the position of the genes along each chromosome can be discovered by assuming that the two genes with the greatest frequency of separation are the farthest apart. It is found, in this way, that genes are always arranged one after another along the length of a chromosome, and in the same order on each chromosome of a pair.

6 THE ARRANGEMENT OF THE UNPAIRED GENES ON THE SINGLE CHROMOSOME OF A BACTERIAL NUCLEUS

We have seen that the genes of the fruit-fly are arranged one after another along its chromosomes. During the last fifty years, genes linked into chromosomes have been found to control the individuality of every living organism whose heredity has been studied, including bacteria and viruses. In higher organisms, as has been seen, almost every gene has a partner in an identical position on a paired chromosome, and the form in which a unit character will appear is decided by the combined action of these two genes. It has been discovered that many lower organisms including bacteria and viruses have unpaired genes linked into a single unpaired chromosome and that the form of each unit character results from the action of one gene. To conclude this chapter, some beautiful experiments will be described which were done in the Pasteur Institute in Paris, and which show that the single chromosomes of *E. coli* bacteria are long and narrow with the genes arranged one after another along them.

To describe these experiments, it is necessary to go back to the surprising discovery of a bacterial sex life made in 1946 by Lederberg and Tatum of Yale University. It had been known for many years that bacteria multiply by cell division, and until 1946 it was believed that bacteria did not mate or come into any significant physical contact with one another. Therefore, it was thought that the genes of any bacterium were derived from only one parent. Lederberg and Tatum showed that this was not so, and that very occasionally two bacteria mate, so mixing their genes, and this mixture is passed on to their progeny. They made this discovery by experiments of which the following is a simplified example. They had two strains of *E. coli* bacteria which differed in two unit characters. The first was able to make its own supplies of the vitamin, biotin, but was unable to make the amino acid leucine. The second could not make biotin but could make leucine. Either strain when incubated alone, with the necessary foodstuffs, multiplied to give many more bacteria, all of which had the same genes as the parent strain (except for a few cells whose genes had changed by a spontaneous process called mutation which will be described in a later chapter). When, however, the two strains were grown together, bacteria occasionally appeared which could make both biotin and leucine (their appearance could not be explained by mutation). In other words, new bacteria had been formed which contained one gene from one parent cell and another from another parent cell. Lederberg and Tatum correctly attributed this to mating between two bacterial cells, and for this discovery, which like most scientific discoveries is simple in retrospect, they have been awarded the Nobel Prize.

In their experiments, only about two in every 2,000,000 bacteria mated successfully with one another, and it is not surprising that Lederberg and Tatum were unable to observe mating under the microscope. Recently, strains which mate successfully 1,000 times more frequently have been discovered and mating has been observed. The two mating bacteria lie side by side and a tube forms between them, and through this tube, genes from the male cell pass into the female. Once in the female cell, the invading genes may interchange with some of the female's genes by a process similar to crossing over in higher organisms. The female cell then breaks away and by division gives new bacteria which, although still containing unpaired chromosomes, contain genes from the two parent cells.

Now, Jacob and his colleagues of the Pasteur Institute were able to make use of this mating to reveal the structure of the E. *coli* chromosome. They showed that, like the chromosomes of higher organisms, it is long and narrow, that its genes are arranged one after another along its length, and that during mating it passes from the male into the female like a rope passing through a narrow hole. Jacob's discovery depended on his finding that mating bacteria, which usually lie side by side for about half an hour, could be broken apart by stirring the solution in which they were suspended in a Waring blender—the machine often used as a household mixer. In his experiments he allowed two strains of bacteria to mate which differed in six unit characters and hence in six genes. If he left them to mate for the full half hour all six genes passed from the male into the female. But if they were broken apart at twenty-five minutes only five genes entered the female. One, which conferred the ability to ferment the sugar, galactose, did not pass in. If separated at eighteen minutes both this gene, and another controlling lactose fermentation, were excluded; if at eleven minutes these two and another conferring immunity to a virus; if at ten minutes these three and another conferring sensitivity to a particular drug; if at nine minutes these four and another conferring the ability to make the nutrient leucine; and if separated at seven minutes all these five genes, plus the sixth which conferred the ability to make the nutrient threonine, did not enter the female. In all experiments the different genes passed into the female in the same order in time. From these experiments Jacob concluded that the genes of E. coli are strung together into a chromosome resembling that of higher organisms and this conclusion has been fully confirmed by other experiments that will not be described.

The Molecular Structure of Genes

4

1 THE CHEMICAL BASIS OF HEREDITY

At the beginning of the last chapter it was promised that a clue to the fundamental problem of cellular heredity—the replication of the molecules of a cell after division—would be provided by Mendel's discoveries. But at first sight, the finding that inherited characteristics can be subdivided into unit characters, each controlled by one or two genes, appears to have little relation to cell molecules. In particular, the various unit characters, such as plant height, seed shape, and flower color in peas, appear so unrelated that a common chemical basis is difficult to conceive. Although the rediscovery of Mendel's work revealed an ordered basis for heredity, how it could be explained in material terms remained mysterious. For example, in 1902 the famous geneticist W. Bateson wrote, in an enthusiastic account of Mendel's discoveries, "Let us recognize from the outset that as to the essential nature of these phenomena we still know absolutely nothing. We have no glimmering of an idea as to what constitutes the essential process by which the likeness of the parent is transmitted to the offspring . . . We do not know what is the essential agent in the transmission of parental characters, not even whether it is a material agent or not. Not only is our ignorance complete, but no one has the remotest idea how to set to work on that part of the problem."

But gradually the experiments of Mendel and his successors were seen to give a clue as to how the replication of molecules after cell division might occur. Living organisms are composed of molecules. Therefore, certain differences in the formation of cell molecules must underlie the different forms which each unit character can manifest. These differences, in accord with Mendel's experiments, result from the action of different genes. Genes, therefore, control the formation of at least some cell molecules. Hence, the simplest explanation of cellular heredity would be that genes, directly or indirectly, control the formation, or entry into the cell, of all other molecules; and that the molecules of which they are themselves composed are in some way capable of forming self-copies. This explanation has been largely verified by the discoveries of molecular biology which will be described in the three remaining chapters. In the present chapter we shall consider the chemical structure of genes, which is a necessary prelude to explaining heredity in terms of chemistry. In the next chapter we shall consider how genes form self-copies, and in the last, how genes control the formation of specific protein molecules. These molecules are the common basis of the diverse

Mendelian unit characters, and through them, genes control the formation of other molecules of the cell.

2   THE MOLECULES OF WHICH CHROMOSOMES ARE MADE

Since genes lie on chromosomes, a first step in discovering the chemical structure of genes can be made by analyzing chromosomes. A. E. Mirsky and his colleagues at the Rockefeller Institute in New York have devised methods for isolating chromosomes from liver, kidney, and some other tissues. The cells in these tissues of an adult animal are mostly not dividing, and their chromosomes cannot be seen with a microscope. They can, nevertheless, be isolated successfully. Their isolation will be described in some detail as it is typical of many biochemical preparations. Although such procedures are simple to perform, to devise them usually requires some years of inspired trial and error in the laboratory.

The piece of liver, or other tissue, is finely chopped with scissors, then added to a salt solution containing chopped ice, and disintegrated in a Waring blender at top speed for six minutes. The suspension is then strained through gauze, and the liquid centrifuged for fifteen minutes at the slow speed of 2,000 revolutions per minute. A sediment separates which is composed of chromosomes and unbroken nuclei. This sediment is dispersed in a salt solution and passed through a colloid mill which breaks almost all the nuclei, liberating the chromosomes. The suspension is centrifuged and the sediment is washed twice on the centrifuge with the salt solution, and then three times with a solution of citric acid. The sediment is then suspended in the citric acid and once more passed through the colloid mill. The suspension is then centrifuged and the sediment washed twice more with the citric acid. The sediment is then suspended in the citric acid and left to stand overnight. The lower part of the suspension is then thrown away and the upper part centrifuged. The sediment which results is the finally purified chromosomes.

Chromosomes isolated in this way can be analyzed chemically. When they are suspended in sodium chloride solution they disintegrate, and if the resulting suspension is centrifuged a small sediment is formed with a clear solution above it. The clear solution contains the bulk of the original chromosomes—from fifty to ninety-five per cent of their original weight, depending on the tissue from which the chromosomes came. The material in this clear solution is forty-five per cent DNA and fifty-five per cent proteins, the proteins being histones, which are peculiar to cell nuclei. The sediment below the clear solution consists mostly of proteins but is about ten per cent RNA. From these analyses the composition of the original chromosomes can be calculated. The figures range from forty per cent DNA, fifty per cent histone and five-tenths of a per cent RNA in the chromosomes from the red blood cells of some fishes, to twenty per cent DNA, twenty-five per cent histone and four per cent RNA in liver chromosomes. The remaining weights of each are miscellaneous proteins. Therefore, the most important components of chromosomes by weight are always DNA and histones. These analyses therefore suggest that genes are most probably made from DNA or histones or both.

3 GENES WHICH PASS FROM DEAD TO LIVE BACTERIA ARE MADE OF DNA

Evidence will now be given that genes of bacteria are made solely from DNA. This evidence comes from a study of bacterial transformation which was discovered by F. Griffith in England in 1927. Pneumonia bacteria, or pneumococci, exist in a number of strains or races. These mostly have a carbohydrate coating, or capsule, surrounding the cell, but some have no capsule. When grown under identical conditions, the bacteria with capsules produce more bacteria with capsules, while those without, produce more bacteria without. The difference in capsule must therefore be a genetic difference, that is, a difference in the form displayed by one or more unit characters.

Griffith was working with two strains of pneumococci: one with capsules which, when injected into mice, multiplied and killed them with pneumococcal infection; and another, without capsules, which multiplied but did not kill the mice. When bacteria with capsules were heated to 60°C they were killed, and no longer infected the mice. But Griffith made a strange discovery. If these dead bacteria were injected together with the live harmless bacteria without capsules, the mice sometimes died of infction; and the blood of these animals was always infested with live harmful bacteria with capsules. These could be isolated and were indistinguishable from the bacteria which had been killed before injection. It must be concluded that something passed from the dead bacteria into the live ones which caused their progeny to possess an alternative form of one or more unit characters: namely to possess capsules and be pathogenic to mice. At least at first sight, it appears that one or more genes must have passed from the dead to the live bacteria.

To try and discover how this bacterial "transformation" took place, other biologists took over where Griffith had left off. They first managed to reproduce the transformation of the pneumococci in a broth culture. Dead bacteria with capsules were added to the broth, which was inoculated with live bacteria without capsules, and then incubated for some hours. A drop of the culture was then diluted and smeared over agar jelly, which contained bacterial nutrients, in flat dishes. (This is a standard technique to deposit separate bacterial cells over the jelly. On incubation, separate colonies appear, each of which is derived from a single cell.) It was found that the bacteria in most of the colonies which formed were without capsules. But about one in a thousand did have capsules, and hence had been transformed.

The next logical step was to extract various chemical components from the dead bacteria and see whether any of these would cause transformation. Experiments of this kind were largely done by O. T. Avery and R. D. Hotchkiss of the Rockefeller Institute. They were, in fact, able to obtain extracts which would cause

transformation, and they fractionated these extracts into different chemical components and tested each in turn. After some
years of work, they announced that one, and one only, type of
chemical compound from the capsulated bacteria would trans-
form some of those without capsules when added to the broth
culture. This compound was DNA which was about ninety-five
per cent pure. Warnings were at once issued by some biologists
that the transformation might be caused by some more subtle
"principle" in the five per cent impurity. These warnings were
justified since many thought DNA to be incapable of existing in
as many structural variations as there are genes in an organism;
but there was also a reluctance to attribute a genetic change to a
chemical compound. However, the evidence has since become overwhelming that the transformation is caused by the bacteria that
do not have capsules absorbing DNA from those which do, in a
manner which is not yet clear. For example, the DNA has been
further purified until it contains negligible amounts of other
compounds, including less than two hundredths of one per cent
protein. Also, the potency of the DNA is rapidly destroyed by
enzymes which break down DNA, but is unaffected by those
that break down RNA or proteins.

How are these experiments to be interpreted? The progeny of
bacteria which are transformed possess unit characters in forms
in which their ancestors did not possess them. Therefore, either
the transforming DNA must contain genes which are responsible
for these forms of the unit characters, or it must activate genes
which lie latent in the recipient cell. It appears certain that the
DNA, in fact, contains the genes. Transforming DNA of many
different kinds has now been isolated, each being specific for
different unit characters. For instance, if DNA from cells which
are resistant to the drug, streptomycin, is added to a culture of
those that are sensitive, some bacteria result which breed resistant
progeny. There seems no reason to believe that transforming
DNA could not be isolated which was specific for any form of any
unit character. The hypothesis that transforming DNA merely

activates pre-existing genes in the recipient cell, therefore, crumbles, since each gene would have to have a specific activator which is reproduced generation after generation. It is difficult to escape the conclusion that in pneumococci, and in a number of other bacteria in which transformation has been demonstrated, genes are made of DNA.

4 VIRUS GENES WHICH PASS INTO BACTERIAL VICTIMS ARE MADE OF DNA

There is also good evidence that the genes of bacterial viruses, or bacteriophages, are made of DNA. The bacterial viruses that have been most studied are those that infect *E. coli* bacteria, and in particular the virus named T_2. The electron microscope shows that T_2 viruses have hexagonal bodies and a protruding tail. When a suspension of these viruses at 37°C is mixed with a suspension of *E. coli*, the viruses can be seen to become attached by their tails to the surfaces of the bacteria, where they remain. About twenty minutes later a spectacular thing happens. The bacteria burst and each releases about one hundred complete new viruses, while the original infecting viruses can still be seen in outline attached to the bacterial membrane. It is clear that some compound (or compounds) passed from the infecting viruses into the bacteria where it caused the formation of the new viruses. This compound must, therefore, have contained the genes of the virus.

A first step to discovering of what compound these genes are composed can be made simply by analysing the viruses. They are found to contain proteins and DNA but no detectable RNA, hence, the genes cannot be made of RNA. Also, only the contents of the infecting viruses pass into the infected cells, and it is possible to release the contents artificially and analyze them. Viruses are suspended in concentrated salt solution and water is then rapidly added. The viruses are burst by the change in osmotic pressure, and their contents are liberated, leaving the hexagonal coats which can be separated by centrifuging. Analyses show that all the DNA of the viruses is liberated when they burst, while most of the protein remains with the coats. This suggests that the genes are made of DNA.

That the virus genes are made of DNA is proved almost conclusively by an experiment performed by A. D. Hershey and M. Chase at the Carnegie Institution in Cold Spring Harbor, New York. They prepared bacterial viruses in which the phosphorus and sulphur was radioactive. They did this by first growing E. *coli* bacteria in a nutrient solution containing radioactive phosphate and sulphate, and then infecting the labelled bacteria with unlabelled viruses. A suspension of the radioactive viruses was then mixed with a suspension of ordinary E. *coli* cells. The viruses attached themselves to the bacteria, but after a few minutes they were broken away again by stirring the suspension in a Waring blender. Nevertheless, when a portion of the suspension was incubated for some minutes more, the bacteria burst liberating the usual number of complete viruses. Hence, some material must have passed from the viruses into the bacteria during the few minutes of attachment, and this material must have contained the virus genes. Hershey and Chase did not incubate most of the suspension after the viruses had been separated from the bacteria. Instead, they cooled and centrifuged it, so separating the bacteria from the remains of the viruses. They then measured the quantities of radioactive sulphur and phosphorus in each. They found that eighty-five per cent of the radioactive phosphorus of the viruses had passed into the bacteria, while eighty per cent of the sulphur was still with the remains of the viruses. Now, the proteins of the virus contain sulphur but almost no phosphorus, while the DNA contains phosphorus but no sulphur, and there are no other important concentrations of phosphorus or sulphur in the virus. The bulk of the DNA must, therefore, have entered the bacteria while the bulk of the proteins did not. The experiments were later refined to show that almost all the DNA of the virus enters the bacterial cell on infection, but only three per cent of the protein. There is, therefore, a strong probability that the virus genes are contained in the DNA which enters the bacterium, rather than in the trace of protein.

5   ARE ALL GENES MADE OF DNA?

The answer to the question that heads this section is, with very little doubt, "Yes—except for the genes of some viruses which are made of RNA." Yet, the direct evidence on which this answer is based is largely confined to experiments on bacteria and bacterial viruses. Why, then, can we feel so confident of our answer? The reason is partly that many pieces of indirect evidence suggest that genes in higher organisms are made of DNA, and these will be discussed in this section. It is also that the chemical processes in all living cells are, in general, very similar. The cells of men and most bacteria, for example, obtain energy by very similar reactions. Therefore, it would not be surprising if heredity, which follows similar laws in all cells, had a common chemical basis. Strong support for the hypothesis that almost all genes are made of DNA also comes from its success in leading to discoveries about the chemical control of unit characters, not only in bacteria and viruses, but also in higher organisms, including man. The discoveries about the chemical basis of heredity, which will be described later, rest firmly on the conclusion that genes in most cells are made of DNA. When a scientific discovery leads to further discoveries in this way, this is good evidence of its truth. (It is something which the "discoveries" of precognition and extrasensory perception have not yet done.)

The indirect evidence that genes in higher organisms are made of DNA is of many kinds. As we have seen, their chromosomes contain DNA, proteins which are largely histones, and variable amounts of RNA. The possibility that genes are made of RNA is made improbable by the fact that sperms contain insignificant amounts of RNA. The possibility that they are wholly or partly made of histones is made unlikely by the fact that the proteins associated with DNA in sperm heads have a different composition from the histones of other tissues, and are not usually called histones for this reason. DNA does not show these variations. It is always found in chromosomes but not in other parts of the cell, which suggests that its function is solely related to heredity. Also, as was mentioned in an earlier chapter, the quantity of DNA in almost every cell of a single species of animal or plant is the same. The most important exception to this rule is that germ cells contain exactly half this amount. This is the situation we should expect to find if each gene is made of a characteristic quantity of DNA, and if germ cells contain half the number of genes of normal cells. Also, DNA from any cell of any member of a single species of animal or plant always contains, as far as can be detected, the same relative amounts of the four nucleotide sub-units. Hence, all cells of similar hereditary origin have DNA of similar composition. Differences in composition of DNA can only begin to be detected as hereditary differences grow wider.

Further support comes from studies of mutation. When living organisms multiply, an individual occasionally appears which possesses a unit character in a form which was not present in its ancestors. This phenomenon is known as mutation and is found in all organisms from viruses to man. An example of a mutation in a higher organism is the birth of lambs with short legs to sheep whose ancestors have all had legs of normal length, or the birth of a hornless calf to cattle whose ancestors all had horns. The mutant forms of these characters, once they have appeared, are continuously inherited according to Mendel's principles. It is, therefore, clear that one or both of the pair of genes which control the unit character have undergone a permanent change. The mutant forms of the characters are usually recessive and before they first appear the organism must inherit two genes of altered structure. Viruses and bacteria, in which only one gene controls each unit character, need inherit only one altered gene for a mutant form of a character to appear.

The frequency with which mutants appear when organisms breed can be increased by certain treatments which alter the chemical structure of DNA. For example, if bacterial viruses are allowed to infect bacteria in a medium containing 5-bromouracil, this compound is incorporated into the DNA of the viruses in place of thymine. As a result, the frequency with which mutants appear in this and subsequent generations of the virus is increased. As yet, there is no evidence of bromouracil increasing the rate of mutation in higher organisms. But X rays and ultraviolet light will do so both in bacterial viruses, and in higher organisms. For example, if X rays are shone onto a collection of fruit flies, the frequency with which mutants appear will be greater than normal when the flies are allowed to breed. In bacterial viruses, these agents presumably act like bromouracil in altering the structure of DNA, hence, there is reason to suppose that they also do this in higher organisms. More direct evidence that they act in this way in higher organisms comes from another experiment. Ultraviolet light of different wave lengths, was shone onto separate samples of pollen grains of corn under controlled conditions. Each sample of pollen grains was used to fertilize corn plants, and the proportion of mutant plants in the progeny was measured. This proportion was found to depend directly on the extent to which the particular wave length of light is absorbed by nucleic acids.

Direct evidence that genes of higher organisms are made of DNA could conceivably come from genetic transformation of the kind discovered in bacteria. In 1957, a claim that this had been carried out successfully in ducks came from France. The workers isolated DNA from the testes and red blood corpuscles of Khaki Campbell ducks. They injected this DNA into nine Peking ducks and three Peking drakes at frequent intervals, starting eight days after hatching. At one year old, eight of the ducks and one drake showed features which were considered to be those of the Khaki Campbell. For instance, the beak, which is orange in the Peking, showed dark patches of similar color to the beak of the Khaki Campbell. Also, the body weights were lower than normal, and approached those of the Khaki Campbell. However, these experiments have been developed no further. It appears probable that they lacked an adequate control: that the Peking ducklings were not pure bred and would have shown Khaki Campbell characteristics whether or not they had been injected with DNA. However, it is not inconceivable that genetic transformation could be brought about by some similar method, and it could be useful in agriculture, since valuable characteristics might be transferred from one species to another.

6   GENES THAT ARE MADE OF RNA

A number of viruses contain no DNA but are composed of RNA and protein only. Examples are poliomyelitis virus, influenza virus, and the virus which causes mosaic disease in tobacco plants. There is very clear evidence, largely from work on tobacco mosaic virus, that the genes of these viruses are made of RNA.

A great advance in the understanding of viruses was made in 1935 when W. M. Stanley reported, from the Rockefeller Institute for Medical Research, "The isolation of a crystalline protein possessing the properties of tobacco-mosaic virus." When tiny quantities of these crystals were inoculated into leaves of tobacco plants they became infected with mosaic disease. After a few days, crystals of the same "protein" could be isolated from the infected leaves in much larger amounts than had been inoculated. Stanley concluded, "Tobacco-mosaic virus is regarded as an autocatalytic protein which, for the present, may be assumed to require the presence of living cells for multiplication."

Many biochemists resisted Stanley's evidence that a virus could be no more than a pure chemical compound, as many had previously resisted evidence that enzymes are proteins. Their skepticism was not entirely unjustified, for in 1931, other workers had claimed the isolation of the same virus in the form of crystals, but these crystals had later been shown to be an inorganic compound which carried the virus as an impurity. As late as 1950, some reputable scientists still felt that Stanley's crystals were most probably a mere carrier of the true virus. However, in 1946, Stanley was awarded the Nobel Prize for his discovery, and the judgment of the awarders is now vindicated, for his crystals were undoubtedly pure tobacco-mosaic virus.

Work on the virus has been continued by H. Fraenkel-Conrat and his colleagues at the Virus Laboratory in Berkeley, California, which was founded by Stanley. Analyses of Stanley's "protein" showed that it was not a simple protein but a ribonucleoprotein, that is, a loose compound between protein and RNA. The electron microscope shows that the individual virus particles, from millions of which each of Stanley's crystals was built up, are tiny rods with protein on the outside and RNA threaded through the center. Fraenkel-Conrat's experiments have been designed to discover whether the genes of this virus are made of RNA or protein or both.

He succeeded in separating the protein and RNA of the virus by mild procedures which left them undamaged. When these were mixed together under the correct conditions they, somewhat surprisingly, reformed the original viruses. This separation and reconstitution was done as follows (once again, years of hard work underlie a simple procedure). The protein was isolated by dissolving a sample of the viruses in alkaline buffer solution and leaving it for two to three days. The bonds between the protein and RNA were broken, and the protein could then be precipitated alone by adding ammonium sulphate solution of the correct strength. The RNA was obtained by another method. The viruses were dissolved in a detergent solution, and left at 40°C for sixteen to twenty hours. The protein was then removed by adding ammonium sulphate solution, so leaving the RNA. Both the protein and RNA appeared not to be infective when inoculated into tobacco leaves. But if 1 ml. of a one per cent solution of the protein was mixed with 0.1 ml. of a one per cent solution of the nucleic acid, together with 0.01 ml. of an acetate buffer, and the mixture left at 3°C for twenty-four hours, the virus was reformed. This was proved by the ability to infect tobacco plants being very largely restored, and by typical virus particles being visible in the electron microscope.

It might be expected from these experiments that the virus genes are made of a combination of RNA and protein, since neither compound alone appeared to be infective. But Fraenkel-Conrat proved in the following way that this is not so. The virus exists in a number of genetically different strains which can be distinguished by their differing effects on plants. He took two of these strains which can also be distinguished by the protein of one containing certain amino acids that the other does not, and isolated protein and RNA from both. He then reconstituted hybrid viruses by combining the protein of one with the RNA of the other, and vice versa. Tobacco plants were then infected with these viruses and the progeny were examined. The result was beautifully clear-cut. Although hybrid viruses were used for infection they were not produced in the plant. Instead, the viruses were of the strain from which the inoculated RNA had been isolated, and their protein contained amino acids characteristic of this strain. It must be concluded that the genes of these viruses are made solely of RNA, that is, that the RNA controls the formation of all the inherited characters of the virus, including its protein of characteristic composition, and also controls the formation of more RNA of identical structure.

This conclusion was later confirmed by the discovery that pure RNA from tobacco-mosaic viruses will, in fact, give rise to normal infection if inoculated alone in sufficient quantity. The virus protein must, therefore, facilitate the infection of the plant without playing an essential role. Normal viruses are formed as progeny, complete with their characteristic protein. Recently, pure RNA has been isolated from a number of animal viruses and shown to be infective. For example, if RNA from polio virus is inoculated into human cells in tissue culture, the cells become infected and die. From these cells can be isolated normal polio virus containing both RNA and protein. The genes of all these viruses must, therefore, be composed of RNA.

7   EVIDENCE THAT ONE BACTERIAL VIRUS GENE DIFFERS FROM ANOTHER IN ITS INTRAMOLECULAR STRUCTURE

We have seen that there is good evidence that the genes of most organisms are made solely of DNA. If we accept that this is so, in what way does one gene differ from another in structure? In theory, it seems that the differences in function of genes could be founded on one of two distinct kinds of chemical difference. First, it is conceivable that all genes of an organism are made of DNA molecules of identical structure, and that their differences in function result from these molecules being arranged in different, and characteristic, patterns. Alternatively, it is conceivable that each gene has DNA of a characteristic molecular structure, on which its specific function depends. Evidence that the second of these alternatives is correct comes from experiments on bacterial viruses performed by S. Benzer at Purdue University.

These experiments were performed on the virus T_4, which is very like T_2 which was described earlier. When this virus is grown by incubating it with a suspension of E. coli cells in a nutritive medium, mutant viruses occasionally appear. A mutant which is found repeatedly is called the rII mutant. It differs from the normal virus in not being able to grow on a certain "strain K" of E. coli, and in forming colonies of an unusual appearance when grown on "strain B" of E. coli in agar jelly. Since each rII virus has a mutant genetic character it must possess a gene which has a different structure to normal. A clue to what this difference in structure can be, comes from Benzer's very important discovery that there is not just one alteration in structure of the gene which gives rise to the rII characteristic, but many. In other words, although rII mutants all look alike, the corresponding gene differs from the normal in these viruses in many different ways. He proved this by experiments in which E. coli bacteria were infected with, on the average, two rII virus particles per cell. If these two viruses were the progeny of a single rII parent, then the progeny of this double infection were (with certain reservations which need not be explained) all rII. But if the two viruses were progeny of rII viruses that had arisen by mutation on two different occasions, then normal viruses would sometimes be found among the progeny. These normal viruses appeared rarely, but they could be easily detected by incubating the progeny with E. coli K cells on which only normal viruses will grow. It must be concluded that part of the gene from one rII virus combined with part from another, to give a gene of normal structure. Hence, changes in structure which produce the rII characteristic must occur in various isolated regions of the gene. It is possible to make rII viruses arise more frequently than normal by treating the parents with certain mutagenic agents discussed in an earlier section. In this way Benzer obtained over 300 rII viruses, which were shown to differ from one another by double infection experiments on E. coli. Hence, the gene associated with this character can exist in at least one normal structure, and in over 300 other distinct structures which are precisely copied when the viruses multiply.

Benzer also made another important discovery. He found that a large number of the 300 odd rII viruses could be arranged in a series which showed the following properties. On double infection in E. coli, virus No. 1 would give rise to normal progeny with any others in the series except virus No. 2; virus No. 2 would do so with any except Nos. 1 and 3; virus No. 3 would do so with any except Nos. 2 and 4, and so on. It must be concluded that the region of structural change in the gene of virus No. 1 overlaps that in the gene of virus No. 2 but not the change in any other virus of the series; and that the structural change in virus No. 2 overlaps that in viruses 1 and 3 but not in the others, and so on. Benzer showed that the many rII viruses which did not fall into this overlapping series would, on double infection of E. coli, give normal progeny with all but one, or a succession, of the members of this series. It is clear that each of the 300 odd genes of abnormal structure must have its structural abnormality in a long or short segment of the length of the gene, and therefore, that the gene must be long and narrow. We could compare the normal gene to a long white rod, and the 300 odd genes of altered structure to white rods of the same length which have been painted red along a short or long segment of their length— the red segment representing the region of altered structure.

We, therefore, have before us the following facts. This particular gene is, like others of the same virus, made of DNA. It is very long and narrow and can exist in over 300 different structural forms, each of which can be precisely copied when the viruses multiply. Also, it is possible to calculate roughly the quantity of DNA in the gene. The total DNA in the virus is about 100 million times the weight of a hydrogen atom. It follows from an estimate of the number of genes in the virus that the weight of each gene cannot be more than a few million on this scale and, hence, can contain only some thousand nucleotides. The almost inescapable conclusion is that the gene is either a whole, or part of a whole, DNA molecule, and that the variations in its structure which cause the appearance of the rII characteristic are changes in nucleotide sequence or spelling along long or short segments of the molecule. It is, therefore, a reasonable working hypothesis that every gene is either a whole, or part of a whole, DNA or RNA molcule, and that one gene differs from the next in its nucleotide sequence or spelling. It will be seen that this hypothesis is fully supported by its ability to explain other facts of genetics in chemical terms.

How Genes Make Copies of Themselves

5

1 WATSON AND CRICK

We have seen that Mendel's discoveries suggested an explanation
of cellular heredity in chemical terms; namely, that genes can
cause copies to be formed of their own component molecules, and
can also, directly or indirectly control the formation, or entry into
the cell, of all other molecules. With the knowledge that genes
are made of DNA, the problem of their self-copying becomes
clearer. Can DNA molecules in fact direct the formation of exact

copies of themselves and, if so, how? It is these questions that will be considered in this chapter.

Throughout the first half of this century the possibility was considered that self-copying, or autocatalytic, molecules exist, but precise ideas of what their structure might be, or how the self-copying reactions might occur, were lacking. Some scientists even built self-copying toys to assure their colleagues that the process was not impossible. Even by 1950, when it had become clear that DNA is probably the one important self-copying compound of living cells, there were no precise suggestions of the chemical reactions by which the process could occur. Then, in 1953, J. D. Watson and F. H. C. Crick, of Cambridge University, tentatively announced the most exciting biochemical discovery of the century. It revealed that DNA molecules occur in nature in loosely bound pairs; and that whatever the spelling of one molecule of each pair may be, it always bears a set relation to that of its partner. The manner in which DNA molecules might form self-copies immediately became clear, and biologists were able to visualise the chemical process which underlies the division and self-copying of living cells, which they had observed under the microscope for many years.

The manner in which Watson and Crick discovered this paired structure of DNA molecules is interesting because it concerns the correct balance between speculation and experiment in scientific research. Watson and Crick in fact performed no experiments on DNA. They made use of the published experiments of others, including those of M. F. H. Wilkins and his colleagues at London University who were also trying to discover how DNA molecules are arranged in nature. But their suggested structure of DNA was largely the result of speculation. They knew that DNA molecules are chains of nucleotides, and they had certain clues from published experiments as to how these chains are arranged in relation to one another. From these facts, and much hard thinking, combined with the building of scale models of DNA molecules, they reached their conclusions about the probable structure of DNA.

Their proposed structure was elegant, and whether true or false, threw great light on the type of chemical reactions by which the self-copying of DNA might occur. But when announced, it was not backed up by sufficient experimental evidence to make it conclusive. Within a few years, their structure was proved to be correct, largely by further careful X-ray diffraction measurements of Wilkins and his colleagues. They, in time, would no doubt have reached the same conclusions as Watson and Crick about the structure of DNA by a more orthodox approach, involving more experiment and less speculation. They could then have announced the discovery with strong experimental support.

Which approach to scientific discovery is the best? Obviously there is no straightforward answer. In the last twenty years most biochemists have tended not to let speculation advance far beyond rigid experimental proof. This approach is largely a reaction against two ill-founded speculative bubbles of the 1930's, the cyclol theory of protein structure and the tetranucleotide theory of nucleic acid structure. However, lack of speculation can sometimes be a form of laziness. To many scientists, experiments are less painful to carry out than concentrated thinking. In the last few years, under the influence of Crick, there has been a tendency for speculation among biochemists to increase, especially in molecular biology. So far, the results appear to be only good. The speculations have been carefully founded, and prophecies that experimental results would be tailored to fit them have not been justified. The Nobel awarders, at least, have made no judgment as to whether speculation or experiment was more important in discovering the paired structure of DNA. In 1962 they awarded a prize for the discovery to Watson, Crick, and Wilkins.

2   CLUES TO THE STRUCTURE OF DNA

When they started their speculations, Watson and Crick had a number of clues as to the way in which DNA molecules are arranged, in relation to one another. First, many experiments had suggested that all samples of DNA are fibrous, that is, that the component molecules are stretched out side by side, and are not coiled into balls like globular protein molecules such as myoglobin, which was discussed in the first chapter of this book. Secondly, experiments had strongly suggested that hydrogen bonds occur in DNA. These are bonds which cannot be explained by the normal rules of valency but can be understood by the theory of resonance. Hydrogen atoms have a valence of one. But if a hydrogen atom is linked by this single valency bond to one of certain other atoms, notably oxygen or nitrogen, it may have the ability to form a weaker bond with still another atom (especially an oxygen or nitrogen atom) in the same or another molecule. As a result, two atoms, such as one oxygen and one nitrogen, become bound together by the hydrogen between them. Such a bond is called a hydrogen bond. A familiar manifestation of hydrogen bond formation is the high boiling point of water. Because of its lower molecular weight, water, H_2O, would be expected to have a lower boiling point than hydrogen sulphide, H_2S. The boiling point is higher because the water molecules are bound together by hydrogen bonds between their oxygen atoms, and a high temperature is, therefore, needed to make the molecules break apart and vaporize. The fact that hydrogen bonds exist in DNA suggested to Watson and Crick that they might bind one DNA molecule to another.

Further experimental evidence also suggested that DNA molecules are arranged in solution so that the phosphate groups of each nucleotide lie exposed to the exterior, while the bases do not. Moreover, X-ray diffraction measurements hinted that, although DNA molecules are arranged lengthways side by side, they are not stretched out as straight as they could be, but are in the shape of long helixes, or corkscrews, and that each helix is made from two molecules.

From these clues, Watson and Crick tried to work out the precise way in which DNA molecules must be arranged in relation to one another. They realized that this arrangement is dictated by the sizes and positions of the constituent atoms. They, therefore, attempted to discover the arrangement by the most direct way. They built scale models of DNA molecules and tried to fit them together so as to satisfy the various clues as to DNA structure.

3 WATSON AND CRICK'S STRUCTURE OF DNA

After some months of pondering, and model building, Watson and Crick hit upon a most remarkable finding. They had discovered that two long DNA molecules could be fitted together side by side in the shape of a single right-handed helix rather like the strands of two-ply knitting wool, and such a structure did have the phosphate groups of each nucleotide on the outside and the bases within. Most of the clues as to DNA structure were, therefore, satisfied. But experimental evidence had suggested that hydrogen bonds are present in DNA, and for the helix to be stable, the two molecules would need to be held together by hydrogen bonds. Watson and Crick found that hydrogen bonds could be formed between oxygen and nitrogen atoms of adjacent bases on the paired molecules, but that these could only be formed between certain pairs of bases.

It will be remembered that the four nucleotides of DNA differ from one another in that their base may be adenine, guanine, cytosine, or thymine. (In some DNA, part of the cytosine has a methyl or hydroxymethyl group on its carbon No. 5. This does not affect any of the points which will be discussed here, and "cytosine" will mean cytosine and these derivatives.) It was found that a nucleotide containing adenine on one DNA molecule would, for reasons of space and orientation, only form hydrogen bonds with the adjacent nucleotide in the paired molecule if this nucleotide contained thymine. Similarly, guanine would form hydrogen bonds only with cytosine. Therefore, if the two molecules in the helix are held together throughout their length by hydrogen bonds between each adjacent pair of nucleotides, the spelling of one molecule must bear a fixed relation to that of the other. Whatever the spelling of one molecule, that of its partner would be given by the following simple rule: for A, substitute T; for T, substitute A; for G, substitue C; and for C, substitute G (where A = nucleotide containing adenine, and so on). Thus, if the spelling along part of one molecule happened to be –A-T-A-G-G-C-, that along the adjacent part of the paired molecule would be –T-A-T-C-C-G.

Watson and Crick found that some strong support already existed for the idea that DNA always occurs with this precise relationship between the spelling of the paired molecules. Careful analyses had recently been made on many samples of DNA from different sources. These had shown that, in any sample of DNA the number of residues of adenine and thymine were always equal, as were those of guanine and cytosine. Any deviations from this rule could be reasonably attributed to experimental error. Thus, DNA from salmon was found to contain adenine, guanine, cytosine, and thymine residues in the relative amounts, 28 to 27 to 20 to 19. In DNA from a certain bacterium these ratios were, 17 to 16 to 25 to 28.

To the biochemists who had made these analyses, the apparent equimolar ratios were something of a skeleton in the cupboard. About ten years earlier, it had been claimed by certain biochemists that samples of DNA always contained residues of the four nucleotides in equal numbers. If the few analyses on which this claim was founded are examined, it is seen that there are quite large deviations from equality. But these deviations were thought to be due to experimental error, and on the basis of the analyses, the tetranucleotide hypothesis was fabricated. It suggested that DNA molecules always have the four nucleotides repeated one after the other, again and again, over their entire length. The painstaking analyses that exploded this hypothesis were the very ones which strongly suggested that adenine and thymine and guanine and cytosine residues occur in equal numbers. However, their discoverers were reluctant to proclaim them with any certainty lest they should fall into the same trap as

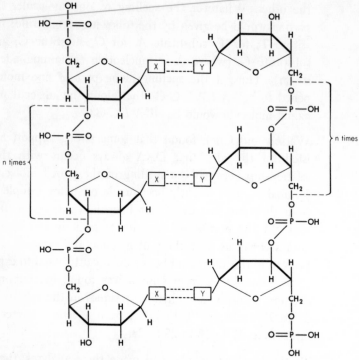

Fig. 19   Chemical structure of two DNA molecules bound together as suggested by Watson and Crick. X and Y represent the bases which are linked by hydrogen bonds. When X is adenine, Y is thymine, and vice versa; when X is guanine, Y is cytosine, and vice versa.

their predecessors. Watson and Crick had no such inhibitions. They saw that the ratios emerged from careful analyses of many DNA samples, and they proclaimed them as strong support for their structure of DNA.

Details of Watson and Crick's structure of DNA are shown in Figs. 19 and 20. It is important to realize that the molecules in each pair run in opposite directions. That is, at either end of the helix, one end of one molecule is aligned with the opposite end of the other. The ends of a DNA molecule can be distinguished because, in the nucleotide chain, the sugar residues are not symmetrically placed. Each sugar is linked by its carbon No. 3 to

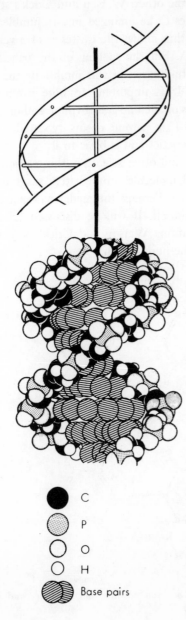

C

P

O

H

Base pairs

Fig. 20 Arrangement in space of two DNA molecules bound together according to Watson and Crick. They are represented in two ways. At the top, the paired molecules are shown as tapes connected by rods, which represent the hydrogen bonds. The vertical rod represents a hypothetical axis around which the paired molecules are wound in a helix. At the bottom, individual atoms of the paired molecules are drawn as they appear in molecular models.

phosphoric acid on the side towards one end of the molecule, and by carbon No. 5 on the other. Watson and Crick's structure allows the four nucleotides to be arranged in any jumbled order along one molecule, and thus allows the existence of a very large number of kinds of DNA. But the spelling of the paired molecule must always be the translation of this jumble by the simple rule already mentioned. It is important to note carefully the pairing by hydrogen bonds of adenine and thymine and of guanine and cytosine (Fig. 21). This pairing occurs repeatedly in the chemical mechanism of genetics and is basic to it.

To Watson and Crick, and other scientists, the relationship in the spelling of the paired molecules immediately suggested how DNA could form self-copies. Perhaps the reader has spotted how this could happen, for himself. It will be discussed fully when some evidence which confirms Watson and Crick's structure of DNA has been given in the next section.

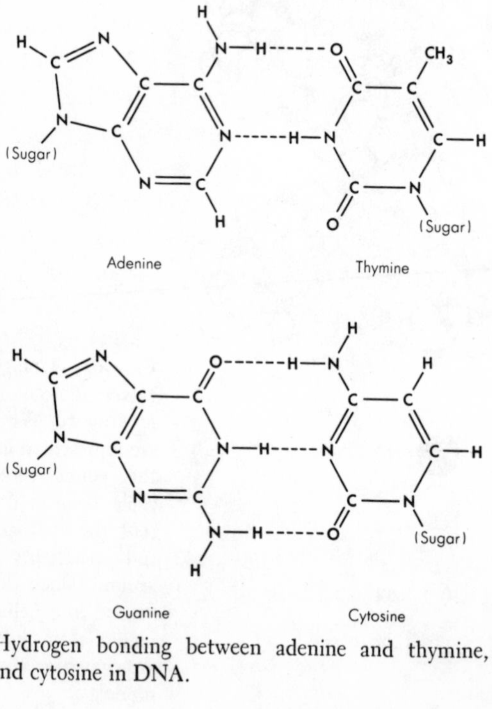

Adenine   Thymine

Guanine   Cytosine

Fig. 21 Hydrogen bonding between adenine and thymine, and guanine and cytosine in DNA.

4 CONFIRMATION OF WATSON AND CRICK'S STRUCTURE

It has now been proved beyond doubt that, in nature, DNA molecules are nearly always arranged in a structure almost identical to that proposed by Watson and Crick. The strongest supporting evidence has been provided by comprehensive X-ray diffraction measurements, made by Wilkins and his colleagues. These show that the distances between some of the atoms of the paired molecules are slightly different from those specified by Watson and Crick, but that the basic structure, which was outlined in the last section, is correct. Comprehensive chemical analyses also show beyond doubt that samples of DNA almost always contain adenine and thymine, and guanine and cytosine residues in equal numbers.

Further evidence that DNA molecules occur in pairs, which are held together by hydrogen bonds as proposed by Watson and Crick, comes from some elegant experiments which were done by C. A. Thomas at Harvard University. Thomas' evidence for the pairing of DNA molecules was based on studies of viscosity. DNA gives very viscous solutions in water, as do other compounds whose molecules are long and narrow and tend to entangle with one another. Normally, if the molecules in a solution of such a compound are gradually made shorter, the viscosity of the solution falls proportionally. DNA molecules can be shortened by incubating them with the enzyme, deoxyribonuclease, which can be isolated from the pancreases of cattle. It catalyzes the breaking of the linkage between two successive nucleotides. It acts more or less at random along the length of the molecule and shows little preference for the long DNA molecules, or for the fragments formed by their breakdown. However, when a solution of DNA is incubated with this enzyme, the viscosity does not fall directly with the number of bonds between nucleotides which are severed. Instead, it remains high for a much longer time than would be expected, and then falls rapidly.

This delayed fall in viscosity can be perfectly explained by the pairing of DNA molecules as suggested by Watson and Crick. To understand why, it is helpful to compare each pair of DNA molecules to a ladder, in which the uprights on either side represent the two DNA molecules, and the rungs represent the hydrogen bonds between adjacent nucleotides. (Unlike ladders, DNA molecules are, of course, coiled into helixes, but this does not affect the argument.) Suppose both uprights of a ladder are sawn through separately, at random somewhere along their length. The ladder will only be shortened in length if both cuts have been made between a single pair of rungs, and the chance of this happening is small. If a series of similar cuts in each upright is made, the chance of a cut occurring opposite one which has already been made, and hence of the ladder being shortened, will increase continuously. The delayed fall in viscosity when solutions of DNA are incubated with the enzyme can be explained on a similar principle. The chance of any two paired molecules being severed between a single pair of hydrogen bonds is small at first, but as incubation proceeds the chance of a breakage occurring opposite one that already exists will increase. Thomas showed that the rate at which the viscosity of DNA solutions falls can be exactly explained in this way, with one reservation. A pair of DNA molecules appears to be shortened in length not only when both are severed between the same pair of hydrogen bonds, but also when the breaks are on either side of a common hydrogen bond. This may be compared to a ladder becoming shortened when the uprights are severed on either side of a common rung which is then torn away.

Other comprehensive evidence in support of Watson and Crick's structure of DNA has come from experiments by P. Doty and his colleagues at Harvard University. They found that if samples of DNA are heated in dilute salt solutions for a few minutes, their properties change in a way that can only be explained by paired DNA molecules becoming wholly, or partly, separated. For example, their appearance in the electron microscope changes. The long, straight, narrow strands become shorter and more irregular as would be expected if the DNA molecules were no longer supported by mutual hydrogen bonding.

At first sight it appears surprising that the paired DNA molecules can be so easily separated from the helical structure, but on considering the forces involved this is not so. That the separated molecules will just as easily recombine to give the perfect Watson and Crick helixes seems at first sight ever more improbable, but on further thought it is clear that the process is not unlike the formation of crystals. Doty realized this, and chose his experimental conditions accordingly. He warmed solutions of the separated molecules to temperatures just below those needed to separate them originally, and the molecules recombined into Watson and Crick helixes. Evidence of this came partly from the molecules regaining their original appearance in the electron microscope, but other elegant proofs were devised, all of which cannot be described. In one experiment, it was found that DNA from a certain strain of bacteria, which was able to cause genetic transformation of a related strain, lost this ability when the paired molecules were separated from one another by heating. When the solution of the separated molecules was warmed to a temperature which was believed to cause them to recombine, the transforming ability was largely restored.

5   THE SELF-COPYING OF DNA "IN THE TEST TUBE"

The importance of Watson and Crick's proposed structure was that it immediately revealed how DNA might direct the formation, within living cells, of precise copies of itself. Suppose that the paired molecules of a DNA helix became separated from one another, by the breaking of the hydrogen bonds which joined them, and that the region of the cell in which this occurred contained each of the four nucleotides, or molecules closely related to them, in solution. These free nucleotides would tend to become attached by hydrogen bonds to the nucleotides of the two separated DNA molecules. Free nucleotides which contained adenine would become bound to those in DNA which contained thymine, and so on. If an enzyme was present which would catalyze the linking together of the free nucleotides when hydrogen bonded to a single DNA molecule, a new DNA molecule of the correct spelling would be formed beside the first. The replication of DNA would occur by each molecule directing the formation of a copy, not of itself, but of the partner from which it had separated. Every DNA molecule would thus depend on a symbiotic relationship with its partner for its spelling to be carried on into subsequent generations of cells.

Does DNA, in fact, form copies, essentially by this mechanism of Watson and Crick? To answer this question it is first necessary to know whether DNA does form self-copies. Overwhelming evidence that it does has recently been provided by A. Kornberg and his associates, and it will be discussed in this section. Their experiments were performed largely at Washington University, St. Louis, and at Stanford University, and for them Kornberg was awarded the Nobel Prize in 1959. The experiments were designed to isolate an enzyme from living cells which would catalyze the replication of DNA "in the test tube." Kornberg chose cells which he considered most likely to contain this enzyme in high concentration: E. coli bacteria which were dividing every twenty minutes and hence rapidly forming DNA. He disintegrated some of these bacteria in a buffer solution, hoping in this way to release the enzyme or enzymes involved in DNA synthesis. He then added the compounds which he thought would most probably be used by the cell to make DNA. These were not the component nucleotides themselves, but these compounds with two additional phosphate groups attached to the phosphate of the nucleotide. From a comparison with similar reactions in living cells, it was expected that these additional phosphate groups would "activate" the nucleotides, which could then combine, under the influence of the enzyme, to give a high yield of DNA, eliminating the additional phosphates in the process.

Kornberg realized that even if these compounds were converted to DNA by the disintegrated bacteria, no increase in DNA would be measurable, because the DNA of the bacteria was being rapidly degraded by other enzymes. He, therefore, incorporated radioactive carbon 14 into one of these compounds and after incubation, he isolated the DNA of the disintegrated bacteria to see if it had gained any radioactivity, and hence if any synthesis had occurred against the tide of degradation. He found only traces of radioactivity, but by subdividing the proteins of the bacteria into a number of fractions, he obtained a fraction which would catalyze the formation of DNA of high radioactivity. This contained the synthesizing enzyme largely separated from the enzymes which caused DNA degradation. He then set about studying the properties of this purified enzyme, which he named DNA polymerase.

He found that it had a property which marked it off from all other enzymes. It would only catalyze the rapid synthesis of DNA when incubated with the diphosphates of all four nucleotides, if a small quantity of DNA was first added as "primer." The primer DNA (which, of course, consisted of paired molecules of related spelling) did not need to come from E. coli. Kornberg produced overwhelming evidence that the DNA which was formed, and which could be over twenty times the quantity of the primer DNA, always consisted of paired molecules of the same length and spelling as the primer DNA. In other words, the enzyme had the unique property of catalyzing the self-copying of the primer DNA.

Kornberg's evidence that the structures of primer and product were always identical, was of many kinds. The relative numbers of the four nucleotides in each were shown to be identical in a number of experiments. For example, when a bacterial DNA, used as a primer, contained adenine, thymine, guanine, and cytosine nucleotides in the ratio 0.65 to 0.66 to 1.35 to 1.34, the product contained them in the ratio 0.66 to 0.65 to 1.34 to 1.37. When the primer was DNA from cattle, in which these ratios were 1.14 to 1.05 to 0.90 to 0.85, those in the product were 1.12 to 1.08 to 0.85 to 0.85. Any differences here between the ratios in primer and product could easily be due to experimental error (as, incidentally, could any deviations from a 1 to 1 ratio between adenine and thymine, and guanine and cytosine nucleotides). Kornberg still found these identical ratios in primer and product even when the molecular ratios between the nucleotide phosphates on which the enzyme acted were varied widely. If one of the phosphates was withheld, virtually no DNA synthesis occurred. It was also shown that the DNA formed by the enzyme had the same molecular weight and viscosity as the primer, and that the viscosity showed the same delayed fall as that of the primer on incubation with deoxyribonuclease. Other evidence was obtained to show that the product contained paired molecules aligned in opposite directions, and that the spelling of the molecules of the primer and product were the same.

The reaction between a nucleotide phosphate and a partially completed DNA molecule is shown in Fig. 22. By this reaction the DNA molecule is increased in length by one nucleotide, and by a series of these reactions a complete molecule is built up. Kornberg's experiments leave no doubt about these facts. On Watson and Crick's hypothesis, this molecule is built up beside one of the paired molecules of the primer DNA which has separated from its partner. The nucleotide which is added at each step is the one which can become hydrogen bonded to the particular nucleotide of the primer which lies beside the end of the partially completed molecule (Fig. 22). It seems certain that this postulated mechanism is basically correct. All of Kornberg's findings are exactly in accord with it, and some supporting evidence will be given in the remaining sections. However, precise details of the replication of DNA are still unknown. In particular, it is not clear to what extent in the living cell the paired molecules of the primer DNA must become separated from one another before replication can begin, and how this separation is brought about.

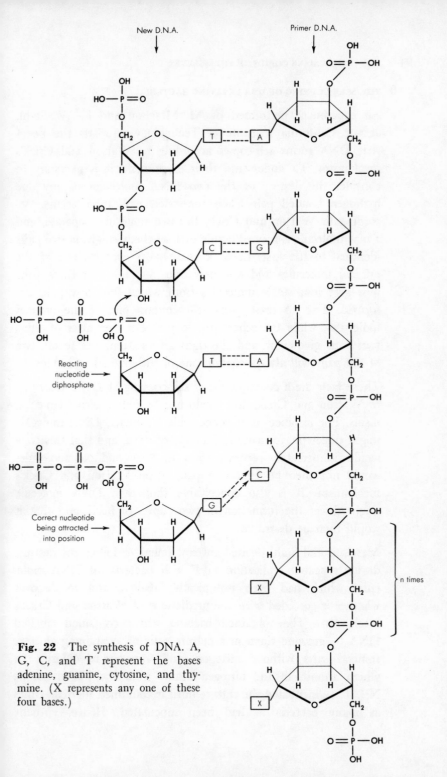

Fig. 22 The synthesis of DNA. A, G, C, and T represent the bases adenine, guanine, cytosine, and thymine. (X represents any one of these four bases.)

6 THE SELF-COPYING OF DNA IN LIVING BACTERIA

An experiment performed by M. Meselson and F. W. Stahl, at the California Institute of Technology, supports the belief that DNA forms self-copies according to Watson and Crick's mechanism. To understand their experiment, it is necessary to consider the destiny of the two DNA molecules of any one hydrogen bonded pair when continued replication occurs. According to Watson and Crick, the two molecules separate, and a new molecule is formed beside each of them, so giving two pairs identical to the first. Each of these pairs contains one of the original molecules and one new one. Suppose that these pairs now give four single molecules from which four new pairs are formed. Two of these pairs still contain one of the original molecules, while the other two do not. For ever after, if these four pairs give eight, and the eight give sixteen, and so on, two of the pairs will always contain one of the original molecules.

These facts are a consequence of self-copying of DNA according to Watson and Crick, and would not be found with all mechanisms. For instance, it is conceivable that each DNA molecule might direct the formation of a copy of itself, and that this copy would immediately separate from it. New and old molecules would not then be bound in pairs as in Watson and Crick's mechanism. It is also conceivable that each DNA molecule might direct the formation of two copies of itself, and that it would then be destroyed.

Meselson and Stahl devised an experiment to follow the destiny, during repeated replication in *E. coli* bacteria, of DNA molecules which had been isotopically labelled, and to discover whether it accorded with the predictions of Watson and Crick's mechanism. They obtained bacteria which contained labelled DNA by growing them in a culture solution containing glucose, mineral salts without nitrogen, and ammonium chloride in which almost all the nitrogen atoms were the heavy isotope N^{15}. They incubated the culture until it contained fourteen times as many bacteria as had been inoculated. Hence, virtually all the nitrogen ($^{13}\!\!\!/_{14}$) in these bacteria was heavy nitrogen. A portion of the bacteria was separated by centrifugation, and their DNA was isolated. To the remainder, a culture solution containing normal ammonium chloride was added in large excess, and the incubation was continued. The bacteria whose DNA contained only heavy nitrogen continued to multiply, and to form new DNA, from ammonium chloride which contained only normal nitrogen. Samples of the bacteria were withdrawn when they had doubled, and further increased in numbers, and DNA was isolated from each.

Meselson and Stahl devised an ingenious way of comparing the densities of the paired DNA molecules in these samples, and their relative contents of heavy nitrogen. If a cesium chloride solution is spun in an ultracentrifuge at a speed which gives 140,000 times the force of gravity, its molecules begin to sediment. However, because their molecular weight is relatively low, they never separate completely. Instead, after twenty hours, a steady state is reached in which the concentration of cesium chloride, and hence the density of the solution, gradually increases towards the bottom of the tube. If DNA is added to the solution before centrifuging, it comes to rest in a band in a region of the tube where its density equals that of the solution. The position of this band can be found by photographing the tube in ultraviolet light. The content of DNA can be found from the extent of the light absorption. It was found that the DNA containing only heavy nitrogen formed a band lower down the tube than did that containing only normal nitrogen.

In this way, they centrifuged their samples of DNA, which had been isolated at various times after the bacteria containing heavy nitrogen had continued their growth in the solution containing normal nitrogen. It will be remembered that one of these samples was isolated after the bacteria had doubled their numbers, and hence doubled their quantity of DNA, in this solution. It was found that this DNA contained particles of only one kind which were intermediate in density between those from DNA containing only heavy nitrogen and only normal nitrogen. This finding is in accord with Watson and Crick's method of replication. This DNA should be composed of hydrogen bonded pairs of one heavy and one light molecule. The DNA isolated after further growth also contained particles of the correct densities in precisely the relative numbers predicted. For example, when the bacteria had quadrupled in number their DNA contained particles of two densities. One-half had the intermediate density, while the remainder had the density of DNA containing only normal nitrogen. It is clear that these experiments exclude certain conceivable methods of DNA replication, and are fully in accord with the mechanism of Watson and Crick. These experiments have since been repeated on the DNA of human cells in tissue culture, and of Chlamydomonas and certain bacterial viruses, with the same results.

7 THE SELF-COPYING OF DNA IN THE CHROMOSOMES
OF HIGHER ORGANISMS

It has been seen in an earlier chapter that the genes of higher organisms are arranged one after another along the chromosomes. Many questions remain unanswered about the structure of chromosomes. Is each gene a distinct pair of DNA molecules, or is it only a segment of a larger pair? Is there only one copy of each gene in a chromosome or are there a number? It is highly improbable that all the DNA known to be present in a chromosome is in the form of one enormous pair of molecules, for two reasons. First, it can be calculated that if this pair of molecules was stretched lengthways it would be some hundred times the actual length of the chromosome. Secondly, if replication of the DNA occurs according to Watson and Crick it is impossible to conceive of paired molecules of this length separating from one another. The most popular model of the chromosome depicts the genes as pairs of DNA molecules aligned side by side, perpendicular to the long axis of the chromosome, with their ends joined together by protein molecules. But this is purely a working hypothesis.

Despite this lack of precise knowledge of the structure of chromosomes, experiments of J. H. Taylor of Columbia University support the belief that their DNA replicates according to the mechanism of Watson and Crick. The DNA of each chromosome doubles in quantity in the period between cell divisions, when the chromosomes are invisible. When they reappear, just before division, each chromosome can be seen to have divided into two daughter chromosomes. Taylor's experiments were designed to discover how the newly formed DNA is distributed between the two daughter chromosomes, and between the chromosomes formed from each of them by subsequent division. He performed his experiments on root tips of plants in which the cells were continually dividing. He immersed these root tips for a short while in solutions of the nucleotide thymidine, which was labelled with radioactive hydrogen, H^3. This is converted into one of the four nucleotides of DNA by plant cells. Taylor left the root tips in this solution long enough for the DNA of many cells to double in quantity, but not long enough for it to double yet again. Any DNA which was formed during this doubling was radioactive. But after removing the root tips from the radioactive solution they were washed so that any DNA formed subsequently would not be radioactive.

The root tips were then left for a few hours to allow some of the pairs of daughter chromosomes, which had been formed in the radioactive solution, to become visible. Did both daughter chromosomes of each pair contain radioactive DNA, or was it confined to one of them? Taylor answered this question by the technique of autoradiography. He flattened the cells on microscope slides and, in the dark, placed photographic film against them. After a while he developed the film. Wherever a chromosome had lain against the film its outline could be seen under the microscope. If this chromosome contained radioactive DNA, its outline was scattered with black dots where radiations had fogged the film. Taylor found that both members of each pair of daughter chromosomes contained radioactive DNA, and counts of the black dots showed that they contained it in equal amounts.

This is the result predicted by the mechanism of Watson and Crick and not by certain other self-copying mechanisms. On Watson and Crick's theory, when every hydrogen bonded pair of DNA molecules in the parent chromosome replicates, it gives two pairs which contain one old and one new molecule each— in this experiment, one inactive and one radioactive molecule. When the pairs of DNA molecules become evenly distributed between the daughter chromosomes, these will acquire equal amounts of radioactivity. Provided certain conditions are fulfilled, Watson and Crick's theory predicts a quite different distribution of radioactivity if these radioactive daughter chromosomes are themselves left to duplicate in a solution which is not radioactive. Suppose that each chromosome contains only one large pair of DNA molecules. In the radioactive daughter chromosomes one member of this pair will be radioactive and the other inactive. When this DNA replicates it will give two pairs, only one of which contains one radioactive molecule. Hence, when this chromosome divides, only one of its daughters will receive a radioactive molecule. If each chromosome contains many pairs of DNA molecules it is possible to conceive of ways in which this uneven distribution of radioactivity would not be found, although replication had occurred according to Watson and Crick. Nevertheless, the uneven distribution is a peculiarity of their mechanism, and, if found, provides good support for it.

Taylor tried to discover whether this uneven distribution of radioactivity among the progeny of the radioactive daughter chromosomes does, in fact, occur. He allowed cells which contained radioactive daughter chromosomes to go through another complete cycle of chromosome duplication in a solution which contained no radioactivity. He then carried out autoradiography when the duplicated chromosomes reappeared. He found that almost all pairs which were formed from a radioactive parent contained one active and one inactive chromosome, in excellent agreement with the predictions of Watson and Crick. Similar experiments have since been made on the chromosomes of human cells in tissue culture with the same results.

How
Genes Control
the Formation
of Other Cell
Molecules

6

1   ONE GENE TO ONE PROTEIN

It has been seen that DNA doubles in quantity between cell divisions by forming self-copies. It will be seen in this chapter that other molecules of cells are not newly formed in this way, but that their formation is either directly or indirectly controlled by the DNA of the genes. This conclusion has arisen largely from the work of G. W. Beadle and E. L. Tatum, at the California Institute of Technology, for which they were awarded the Nobel Prize in 1958. Their experiments were designed to discover how each gene exerts its effect on a genetic character, and suggest that the primary action of each gene is to control the formation of a protein of specific structure.

The first clue to this action of genes came around 1909 from investigations by Sir A. E. Garrod in England on "inborn errors of metabolism," namely, diseases which certain people inherit in which certain chemical reactions of the body are abnormal. An example is alcaptonuria, in which the urine turns black in air because it contains an abnormal compound, homogentisic acid. Garrod gave evidence, from the occurrence of the disease in families, that it is the recessive form of a single unit character. He suggested that homogentisic acid is always produced in the body but is normally converted to some other compound. Thus, the dominant form of the character would be the ability to bring about this conversion. Garrod made the important suggestion that in this and similar diseases, "the most probable cause is the congenital lack of some particular enzyme, in the absence of which a step is missed, and some normal metabolic change fails to be brought about." However, he did not formulate a general hypothesis that a dominant gene acts by controlling the formation of a particular enzyme, or that a recessive gene is faulty in this respect. It is probable that he considered this action limited in extent.

In 1935 Beadle began experiments directly designed to discover the chemical reactions by which genes control inherited characters. He first studied eye color in the fruit fly, and obtained evidence that each gene involved controls one chemical reaction by which eye colors are formed. However, he made more rapid progress a few years later when he collaborated with Tatum. The difficulty of studying most inherited characters in this way is that although they must result from the formation of chemical compounds these are unknown, and must be discovered before the primary chemical action of the genes can be investigated. Tatum

and Beadle decided to circumvent this difficulty by studying inherited characters which are themselves clear-cut chemical reactions, namely, the ability to make certain vitamins and amino
acids from simpler compounds. For their experiments they chose
the mold Neurospora, which has seven pairs of chromosomes on
which the position of a gene can readily be found by breeding
experiments. Neurospora grows well on a simple solution of cane
sugar and inorganic salts, together with one vitamin, biotin. All
other vitamins, and all amino acids, must, therefore, be made
within the mold from the simple components of the growth solution, and the mold inherits the genes which enable it to do this.

Tatum and Beadle decided to try and put some of these genes
out of action and study the effect on the reactions by which
these compounds are formed. They did this by shining X rays or
ultraviolet light onto spores of the mold before sexual reproduc-
tion, and found that some of the progeny were unable to grow
unless an extra vitamin, or a certain amino acid, was added to
the growth solution. These molds had clearly lost the ability
to perform one or more of the reactions by which these compounds are formed, owing to the mutation of one or more genes.
It was found that a number of distinct strains could be isolated
which required the same vitamin or amino acid, and which had
mutations on different genes. It was clear that a number of
genes were concerned in the formation of any one of these
compounds. Tatum and Beadle, and many other workers, concluded that these genes each controlled the formation of a
distinct enzyme. The evidence for this conclusion is varied but
the following is a small and simple part of it. Three strains of
the mold were isolated which required the amino acid arginine
and, hence, could not make it from the simple components of
the growth solution. Each strain had a mutation on a different
gene. One of the strains would grow if arginine, or the amino
acids citrulline or ornithine were added. Another would grow
with arginine or citrulline but not with ornithine, while the
third would grow only with arginine. It was known that, in

liver, arginine is formed from citrulline, which is formed from ornithine, and it was proved that the same reactions occur in Neurospora. Hence, there is a strong suggestion that the first strain lacks the ability to make ornithine, the second to convert ornithine to citrulline, and the third to convert citrulline to arginine.

On the basis of such experiments, Beadle proposed a "one gene–one enzyme" hypothesis: that each gene has a single primary function, namely, to control the formation of one, and only one, specific enzyme. He later modified it to a "one gene–one protein" hypothesis when it became clear that some genes control the formation of specific proteins which are not enzymes. It seems that the hypothesis is, with certain reservations, correct, and applies to all living organisms from viruses to man. In the few instances in which two genes appear to be directly concerned in the formation of one protein, an explanation can be found which does not violate the hypothesis. For example, there is, in E. coli, an enzyme tryptophan synthetase which is composed of two proteins. (The "enzyme" is, in effect, two enzymes that will only act in association.) A mutation in either of the two genes controlling the formation of these proteins can render the bacteria unable to perform the reactions catalyzed by them. But some of the mutant strains have the ability to catalyze these reactions restored if a second "suppressor" mutation occurs at a quite different gene. It at first appeared that this second gene might also be specifically concerned in the formation of one of the enzyme proteins, but experiments of C. Yanofsky of Stanford University show that it is not. It appears that the second mutation results in the structure of "transfer" RNA molecules being altered. They are concerned in the incorporation of amino acids into all proteins, and are discussed in a later section. As a result of their altered structure, incorrect amino acids may occasionally be inserted into proteins. With most proteins this is usally detrimental, and the molecules formed are unable to function normally. But in E. coli mutants which already form defective molecules of tryptophan synthetase this insertion of an incorrect amino acid can occasionally, by chance, give rise to an active enzyme.

An important reservation to the one gene—one protein hypothesis is that some genes do not appear to be primarily concerned with the control of unit genetic characters through the formation of specific proteins. Instead, they regulate other genes, a function which will be discussed in a later section; whether they do so by forming a specific protein is not yet clear. Another reservation is that a few genes in each cell appear to direct the formation of the RNA of the ribosomes and of the cell solution, but not the formation of proteins.

2 A GROUP OF NUCLEOTIDES TO ONE AMINO ACID

Proteins differ from one another in the length and spelling of their amino acid chain or chains. Beadle's hypothesis, therefore, implies that the DNA of each gene in some way directs the formation of an amino acid chain of a specific length and spelling. If the structure of the DNA is altered by mutation, then either a protein of altered structure, or no protein at all, will be formed. Evidence will be given in this section that different mutations in a gene can result in alterations of spelling in different small sections of a protein molecule. This evidence leads to precise suggestions as to how the DNA of a gene directs the formation of a protein.

The first evidence for the effect of an alteration in gene structure on the spelling of the corresponding protein came from the work of Sanger and his colleagues which was discussed in Chapter One. They found that the spelling of cattle, pig, sheep, horse, and whale insulin was identical except for amino acids 8, 9, and 10 of the amino acid chain which ends in glycine. Amino acid 8, which is alanine in cattle and sheep insulin, is theonine in that of the pig, horse, and whale. Amino acid 9 is serine in cattle, pig, and whale insulin, but glycine in that of the sheep and horse. Amino acid 11 is valine in cattle and sheep insulin, but isoleucine in that of the pig, horse, and whale. The most probable explanation for these differences is that, during the evolution of each of these animals from a common ancestor, the gene which determines the spelling of this amino acid chain of insulin has undergone one or more mutations. These mutations have resulted in changes in spelling of a small part of the insulin molecule. The fact that the changes are limited to amino acids 8, 9, and 10 of one chain might suggest that mutations can only alter the spelling in a limited part of a protein. Evidence that this is not so will soon be given. It is probable that mutations can change the spelling in other parts of the insulin molecule, but that such insulin is defective. Animals which possess it produce fewer offspring than the average, and, so, the mutant gene is eliminated by natural selection.

Comprehensive studies have been made of the effects of mutation on the spelling of the protein hemoglobin. This is contained in the red corpuscles of blood, and it transports oxygen around the body. Each molecule of hemoglobin contains four amino acid chains. Two of these, called the α chains, are identical and each contains 141 amino acids; while the other two, the β chains are also identical and each contains 146 amino acids. Most people share the spelling of the α chains, and of the β chains, in common with one another, but a few people have chains of abnormal spelling. The first abnormality was discovered by V. M. Ingram of Cambridge University when he investigated the hemoglobin from patients with sickle-cell anemia. In this disease the ability of the hemoglobin to transport oxygen is defective, and it differs slightly in other properties from normal. Ingram showed that this sickle-cell hemoglobin differs from the normal in only one amino acid: the sixth amino acid in the β chains is valine instead of glutamic acid.

That this difference in structure is due to an alteration in the structure of a single gene, is confirmed by studying the inheritance of the protein. If a person with sickle-cell anemia marries a normal person, the red blood corpuscles of their children all contain roughly half normal hemoglobin and half sickle-cell hemoglobin. This suggests that they have inherited a normal gene from one parent, and a gene of altered structure from the other. This is confirmed by studying the distribution of normal and sickle-cell hemoglobin in the red corpuscles of the grandchildren. Recently, seven other kinds of hemoglobin with one abnormal amino acid in the β chain have been isolated from different people, and they are inherited in a similar way. The altered amino acids are numbers 6, 7, 26, 63, 63, 67, and 121 respectively. Hence, the gene can possess at least eight different abnormalities of structure which cause an alteration in one of the 146 amino acids at different points along the β chain.

Five hemoglobins have also been found which have an altered amino acid in positions 16, 30, 57, 58 and 68 respectively of the α chain. Again, these abnormal proteins are inherited in a way which shows that they result from the inheritance of a gene of altered structure. A woman has even been found whose hemoglobin contained both the normal α chain and a roughly equal amount of an abnormal α chain, together with the normal β chain and a roughly equal amount of an abnormal β chain. She married a man with normal hemoglobin and the distribution of that different genes on different chromosomes control the spelling normal and abnormal proteins among their children has shown of the α and β chains. On the "one gene–one protein" hypothesis, these must, therefore, be considered as separate proteins.

H. G. Wittmann of the Max Planck Institute in Germany has also made a comprehensive study of the effects of mutation on the spelling of the protein formed by tobacco-mosaic virus. It will be remembered that the virus is composed solely of protein and RNA, and that the genes of the virus are made of RNA. Wittmann studied the effects of treating the RNA of the virus with nitrous acid before infection. This compound can react with adenine, cytosine, and guanine of the RNA nucleotides, converting their $-NH_2$ groups to $-OH$. If the RNA is left only briefly in contact with nitrous acid, so that only one or a few nucleotides per molecule react, it will still infect tobacco leaves. But the lesions which are formed often look different from normal, and from them mutant strains of the virus can be isolated. These strains can be multiplied within the leaves of the plant and their proteins isolated. Wittmann has isolated twenty-nine proteins from different viruses in which one amino acid somewhere along the chain of 157 was different from normal, and six proteins in which two amino acids were different.

What may we conclude about the manner in which a gene directs the formation of a protein? Benzer's experiments, which will be remembered from an earlier chapter, suggest that a mutation is a change in spelling in a limited segment of the DNA of a gene. From the facts which have been presented in this section, it will be clear that such changes in the spelling of DNA result in a change in spelling in a limited segment of the corresponding protein. These observations strongly suggest that, just as one gene is responsible for the formation of one particular protein, so one group of nucleotides within the gene is responsible for the insertion of one particular amino acid into the protein. This hypothesis will be considered in more detail in the next section.

3   THREE NUCLEOTIDES TO ONE AMINO ACID

Precisely how a group of nucleotides is able to direct a certain amino acid into a protein will be considered in later sections. In this section we shall consider how many nucleotides occur in each group, and how the nucleotides of one group are distinguished from those of adjacent groups. A problem which arises is that a gene is not whole or part of a single DNA molecule, but of a pair of molecules joined by hydrogen bonds. It will be assumed that only one molecule of a gene directs the formation of a protein. Evidence has recently been obtained that this is correct, but it will not be discussed here.

The simplest version of the hypothesis we are considering would be if each nucleotide in DNA directed one specific amino acid into a protein. For example, suppose that the nucleotides containing adenine (A), guanine (G), cytosine (C), and thymine (T), caused the insertion of the amino acids serine (S), proline (P), valine (V), and leucine (L), respectively. Then, if the DNA of a gene began with the spelling A-A-G-C-A-T-, it would direct the formation of a protein molecule which began with the spelling S-S-P-V-S-L- and contained the same number of amino acids as there were nucleotides in the gene. But it can be seen that, because DNA contains only four kinds of nucleotide, this coding relation could only result in proteins which contained four kinds of amino acid.

It would also be impossible for specific pairs of nucleotides to direct each kind of amino acid because the corresponding protein could contain only sixteen amino acids. This is because the nucleotides can be arranged in only sixteen combinations:

A-A, A-G, A-C, A-T, G-G, G-A, G-C, G-T, C-C, C-A, C-G, C-T, T-T, T-A, T-G, and T-C. However, triplets of nucleotides could direct twenty amino acids into protein chains because they can be arranged in sixty-four combinations. Possibly only twenty of these combinations would direct amino acids, but with more than one combination corresponding to each amino acid, possibly more would.

In theory, therefore, the simplest possible coding relation between DNA and protein would be if a succession of nucleotide triplets from one end of the DNA of a gene to the other determined the succession of amino acids in a protein. For example, suppose the gene began with the spelling A-A-T-G-C-A-C-C-A-. Then the triplet A-A-T- would determine the first amino acid, -G-C-A- the second, and -C-C-A- the third. In this code, the triplets are counted off in threes from the first nucleotide in the DNA, that is, the members of each triplet are determined solely by their position relative to the first nucleotide. This coding relation was thought out by Crick and others on the basis of evidence of the kind presented in the first two sections of this chapter. They also devised more ingenious codes in which the members of each triplet are determined in other ways. One suggested that every fourth nucleotide is a "comma." Another said that the nucleotides of one triplet could not be confused with those of an adjacent triplet because the spelling of the resulting triplets did not correspond to any amino acid. Overlapping codes were also suggested in which the end of one triplet of nucleotides forms the beginning of the next. For example, in the sequence given above, an overlapping code would be one in which the triplet A-A-T determined the first amino acid, and -A-T-G or -T-G-C- determined the second. However, experiments (which will be described in this section) of F. H. C. Crick, S. Brenner, and their colleagues, suggest that the code which has arisen in nature is the simplest one.

Evidence is first needed that the code is not overlapping, and this comes from the experiments of Wittmann on tobacco-mosaic virus, which were described in the last section. By chemical treatment he altered isolated nucleotides in the RNA of the virus, and found that usually only one amino acid in the protein became changed. If two amino acids were changed, they were never adjacent. This would not be found in an overlapping code in which a nucleotide in one group can also form part of an adjacent group, and so be concerned in directing more than one amino acid. It may also be concluded that the code in human beings is not overlapping because all abnormal hemoglobins have changed in only one amino acid.

Crick's experiments suggest that groups of three nucleotides direct each amino acid, and that the members of each group are determined by their position relative to the first nucleotide of the gene. They performed their experiments on the T_4 bacterial virus and its rII mutants using the techniques developed by Benzer, which have already been described. It will be remembered that rII mutants of the virus will not grow on E. coli bacteria of strain K, and that they produce colonies of unusual appearance when grown, in agar jelly, on *E. coli B*. It will also be remembered that, although these *r*II mutants look alike, they have been proved by Benzer to be of many kinds, each with a structural change in a different limited segment of the gene. Crick's experiments are founded on the discovery by Benzer that, by double infection of *E. coli*, the structural defects in the genes of two viruses can be combined to give progeny which contain both these defects in one gene, a process known as recombination.

The interpretation of these experiments involves a number of assumptions which are justified by the way in which they produce clarity out of what would otherwise be a chaos of observations. Crick and colleagues selected about eighty distinct *r*II mutants of the T_4 virus which, it was concluded, had one nucleotide missing from their DNA, or one extra nucleotide inserted into it, at some point. The gene of each virus was, therefore, one nucleotide longer or shorter than normal. Some of the viruses had been produced by the action of a chemical which is believed to cause mutations in this way; but the conclusion that a nucleotide had been inserted or removed was largely founded on the following property of the viruses. It was found that they could be divided into two groups. If the structural defects in any two viruses of one group were combined into one gene, the progeny were, like their parents, all *r*II mutants which would not grow on *E. coli K*. But, if the defects in viruses of the different groups were combined, progeny were often produced which showed a surprising property. They would grow on *E. coli K* and formed colonies on *E. coli B* which *more or less* resembled those of the normal virus. In *r*II mutants, it is generally assumed that an unidentified protein is usually lacking, owing to damage of the gene. Crick and colleagues concluded that the viruses which would now grow on *E. coli K* contained a protein which *more or less* resembled the normal one. This protein was formed because the gene had been brought back to its normal length by combining the region lacking a nucleotide in a virus of one group, with the region containing an extra nucleotide in a virus of the other group. The reason why this could result in the formation of a protein of more or less normal structure is as follows.

It must be assumed that the nucleotides which fall into a single group are determined solely by their position relative to the first nucleotide of the gene. It is on this assumption that the argument is founded. Suppose, for simplicity, that the normal protein, which is lacking in the *r*II mutants, contains only one kind of amino acid which is directed into the protein by the group of nucleotides -T-A-G- (the size of the group is immaterial to the argument, but has been assumed to be three). Then the DNA of the gene will consist merely of this sequence repeated throughout its length, with three times as many nucleotides as there are amino acids in the protein:

T - A - G - *T* - A - G - *T* - A - G - *T* - A - G - *T* - A - G - and so on.
 1   2   3   4   5   6   7   8   9 10 11 12 13 14 15

Suppose also that one *r*II virus lacked the fourth nucleotide in this gene, and that another had an extra nucleotide (A) inserted between the seventh and eighth. Then the spelling of these genes would be:

T - A - G - *A* - G - T - *A* - G - T - *A* - G - T - *A* - G - *T* - and so on,
 1   2   3   5   6   7   8   9 10 11 12 13 14 15 16

T - A - G - *T* - A - G - *T* - A - A - *G* - T - A - *G* - T - A - and so on.
 1   2   3   4   5   6   7   8   9 10 11 12 13 14

In each of these abnormal genes the nucleotides have been numbered according to the position they occupied in the normal gene. In each gene the first member of each group of three nucleotides has been shown in bold face type. It will be seen that in the abnormal genes, after the point of deletion or insertion of a nucleotide, the triplets have become A-G-T and G-T-A, respectively. Hence, incorrect amino acids, or no amino acids at all, will be inserted by these triplets into the protein which, if formed, will have a structure very different from normal. Therefore, viruses with either of these genes would be expected to be *r*II mutants.

However, if by double infection nucleotides 1 through 5 of the gene of the first virus were combined with nucleotides 6 onwards of the second, a virus would be formed whose DNA had the original length, and the spelling:

T - A - G - *A* - G - T - *A* - A - G - *T* - A - G - *T* - A - G - and so on.
 1   2   3   5   6   7   8   9 10 11 12 13 14 15

It can be seen that, after the second alteration, the correct triplet *T*-A-G is restored. Provided the incorrect triplets do correspond to some amino acid, a protein will be formed which has only incorrect amino acids along a limited segment of the molecule. If the deletion and insertion of nucleotides are not too far apart, it is reasonable to assume that the spelling of the protein which is formed will be normal enough to allow the virus to grow on *E. coli* K. In support of this, it was found that the viruses would not infect *E. coli* K. if the deletion and the insertion were more than a certain distance apart on the gene (their positions having been found by the mapping techniques of Benzer).

The experimental observations of Crick and his colleagues may, therefore, be explained, if it is assumed that the nucleotides which fall together into a single functional group are determined solely by their position relative to the first nucleotide of the gene. Hence, the experiments provide some support for these assumptions. But the argument is tenuous and may appear unconvincing. However, it is supported by a further discovery which makes the experiments difficult to interpret in any other way, and which strongly suggests that there are three nucleotides to each group which directs an amino acid into a protein. It was mentioned that if viruses which had two nucleotides more or less than normal in the gene were produced by recombination, they were always *r*II mutants. The brilliant discovery was made that if viruses which had three nucleotides more or less than normal were formed by further recombination, they would often grow on *E. coli* K and form more or less normal colonies on *E. coli* B. This can be explained by combining the previous assumptions with the assumption that there are three nucleotides to each functional group. Suppose that three *r*II viruses lack the fourth, eighth, and tenth nucleotide, respectively. The spelling of their genes will be:

T - A - G - *A* - G - T - *A* - G - T - *A* - G - T - *A* - G - T - and so on.
1   2   3   5   6   7   8   9 10 11 12 13 14 15 16

T - A - G - *T* - A - G - *T* - G - A - *T* - G - A - *T* - G - A - and so on,
1   2   3   4   5   6   7   9 10 11 12 13 14 15 16

T - A - G - *T* - A - G - *T* - A - G - *A* - G - T - *A* - G - T - and so on.
1   2   3   4   5   6   7   8   9 11 12 13 14 15 16

After each deletion, incorrect triplets are repeated over the whole length of the genes. Suppose, now, that the three deletions are combined into one gene. Its spelling would be:

T - A - G - *A* - G - T - *G* - A - G - *T* - A - G - *T* - A - G - and so on.
1   2   3   5   6   7   9 11 12 13 14 15 16 17 18

It can be seen that after the third deletion the correct triplet is restored for the remainder of the gene. Hence, the gene might be expected to form a protein normal enough in spelling to allow growth on *E. coli* K. The same conclusion is reached if three insertions are combined, or if the spelling of the DNA and the protein is more complex than in this simple example.

4   MESSENGER RNA

It has been seen that every three nucleotides along one of the paired DNA molecules of a gene probably controls the insertion, by some chemical mechanism not yet considered, of one amino acid in the molecule of the corresponding protein. Before considering the chemical details of this process it is logical to ask, "Which triplet of nucleotides corresponds to each of the twenty amino acids which can appear in proteins?" But in fact, it is not possible to describe the recent discoveries which bear on this question until more details of the way in which genes control protein synthesis have been considered.

We might expect to find that proteins are formed in direct contact with genes, but in fact, most proteins are not. They are formed on the tiny particles of the cytoplasm called ribosomes, which were described in Chapter Two. This fact was discovered in the 1950's in experiments by H. Borsook and his colleagues at the California Institute of Technology, and P. C. Zamecnik and his colleagues at Harvard University. Borsook realized that the way to find at which point amino acids are incorporated into proteins, in the cells of higher animals, was to inject a radioactive amino acid into an animal and kill it a few minutes after the injection. After this short time, the only proteins to contain large amounts of the radioactive amino acid would probably be those at the site of protein formation. He, therefore, injected a radioactive amino acid into a guinea pig. Thirty minutes later he killed it and disintegrated its liver in a sugar solution. He centrifuged the resulting suspension at three different speeds and obtained the liver cell nuclei, the mitochrondia, the microsomes, and the supernatant liquid. He discovered that the protein of the microsomes had over twice as much radioactivity per gram as the protein of any of the other fractions. The microsomes, therefore, seemed to be the point in the cell at which amino acids are converted into proteins, and other experiments confirmed this.

In 1950, when Borsook did this experiment, it was not known that microsomes are not true cell structures, but are fragments of the endoplasmic reticulum to which ribosomes are attached. When this fact was discovered a few years later, P. C. Zamecnik and his colleagues attempted to find whether proteins are built up on the ribosomes or on the remainder of the endoplasmic reticulum. In each of a series of experiments, they anesthetized a rat, opened its abdomen and exposed its liver. They then injected a solution of a radioactive amino acid into its tail vein. Then, between two and twenty minutes later, they rapidly removed part of the liver and plunged it into ice water. They then separated the microsomes and washed them with a solution of a detergent which frees the ribosomes, which they then separated by centrifuging. They found that, two minutes after injecting the radioactive amino acid, the ribosomes contained up to seven times more radioactivity in every milligram of protein than the remainder of the microsomes. This difference in radioactivity persisted for several minutes after the injection. It seemed clear that proteins were formed on the ribosomes. Later experiments have fully supported this conclusion, and have shown that proteins are also formed on ribosomes in other organisms including bacteria.

Because proteins are formed on ribosomes, rather than directly on the genes, it follows that each ribosome must carry some kind of precise copy of a gene, in contact with which, amino acids are assembled into proteins of the correct spelling. Since over half the weight of a ribosome is RNA, it at first seemed probable that this RNA would carry an imprint of the gene by its spelling being directly related to that of the DNA. It will be remembered that when DNA forms self-copies, the paired molecules separate and new molecules are formed beside them according to the following rule: *where nucleotides with the bases* A, G, C, *or* T, *occur in one molecule, then those with* T, C, G, *and* A, *respectively, will occur in the new molecule.* This process results from the hydrogen bonding between the bases A and T, and the bases G and C. It will also be remembered that the nucleotides of RNA are very similar to those of DNA, except that one of the four kinds carries the base uracil (U) instead of thymine. It can be proved, by building molecular models, that a nucleotide with the base A will as readily form hydrogen bonds with a nucleotide with the base U, as with one with the base T. Therefore, it seemed reasonable that the RNA of each ribosome would consist of single or paired molecules, built up in contact with one or both molecules of the DNA of a gene according to the following rule: *where nucleotides with the bases* A, G, C, *or* T, *occur in a DNA molecule, those with* U, C, G, *and* A, *respectively, will occur in the RNA molecule.* For example, if the spelling of part of the DNA molecule happened to be A-A-G-C-T-, that of the corresponding part of the RNA molecule would be U-U-C-G-A.

The theory that the RNA of the ribosomes is related to the DNA of the genes in this way can easily be tested in bacteria. In bacterial cells, unlike the cells of animal and plant tissues in which many genes must be inactive, almost every gene of every cell must have, on a ribosome, a replica of itself which is directing the formation of proteins. If the theory is correct, the ratio $\frac{G + C}{A + T}$ in the DNA of each species of bacteria, should, at least roughly, equal the ratio $\frac{G + C}{A + U}$ in the ribosomal RNA. In fact, it does not, as was first discovered by A. N. Belozersky of Moscow State University. He and his colleagues determined these ratios in the total DNA and RNA of twenty-one species of bacteria. The ratio of $\frac{G + C}{A + T}$ in the DNA ranged from 0.45 to 2.73. That of $\frac{G + C}{A + U}$ in the RNA ranged only from 1.03 to 1.45. The bulk of the RNA in these bacteria is ribosomal RNA. If the RNA of the ribosomes themselves is analyzed, the correspondence is no closer.

The theory can only be saved if it is assumed that only a small part of the ribosomal RNA is a replica of the genetic DNA, and this, in fact, appears to be the situation. This RNA has been named "messenger RNA" because it transports a replica of the spelling of the genes into the cytoplasm. It was first detected by E. Volkin and L. Astrachan of Oak Ridge National Laboratory in *E. coli* bacteria which had been infected with T_2 or T_7 viruses, in the following experiment.

The bacteria were grown in an aerated culture solution and, at the height of growth, a suspension of one of the viruses was added, followed immediately by a solution of sodium orthophosphate containing radioactive P^{32}. Then, at short intervals, samples of the infected bacteria were taken and the RNA was isolated. The quantity of RNA did not increase perceptibly after infection, but all four of the component nucleotides acquired radioactive phosphorus showing that a small quantity of RNA had, in fact, been formed. After infection with T_2 virus, the quantity of radioactive phosphorus acquired by the nucleotides containing A and U averaged about 1.7 times that acquired by those containing G + C. It may be concluded that the ratio $\frac{A + U}{G + C}$ in the newly formed RNA was roughly 1.7. The ratio in the RNA formed after infection with the T_7 virus was much lower, namely, 1.2. The ratio $\frac{A + T}{G + C}$ in the DNA of the T_2 and T_7 viruses was found by chemical analysis to be 1.87 and 1.11, respectively. There was, therefore, good evidence that after infection, RNA is formed within the bacteria whose spelling replicates that of one or both of the paired DNA molecules of the infecting virus.

Subsequent experiments, which there is not space to describe, have shown that this messenger RNA, which is formed in *E. coli* bacteria after virus infection, becomes attached to ribosomes which have been formed by the bacteria before infection. On these ribosomes, proteins peculiar to the virus are formed. It has also been shown that when *E. coli* bacteria grow normally, their own DNA continually forms messenger RNA which becomes attached to the ribosomes. Its quantity is small compared with the remainder of the ribosomal RNA, and it is continually broken down and replaced by fresh messenger RNA sent out by the genes.

Moreover, the enzyme which catalyzes the formation of messenger RNA has been isolated from *E. coli* bacteria and named RNA polymerase. It resembles, but is distinct from, the enzyme which catalyzes the self-copying of DNA which was discussed in an earlier chapter. When it is incubated with the diphosphates of the four nucleotides of RNA, RNA is formed but only if a small quantity of DNA is added as primer. The spelling of the resulting RNA molecules replicates that of this primer DNA. The enzyme has also been found in higher organisms, including the rat. In these organisms it appears that messenger RNA can be more stable than in bacteria, and can continue to function on the ribosomes for a longer time.

5   BREAKING THE CODE

It, therefore, appears that messenger RNA on ribosomes guides amino acids into proteins of the correct spelling, and that each molecule of messenger RNA has the same number of nucleotides as the DNA on which it was formed, and a related spelling. It may be concluded from this, and from experiments discussed earlier in this chapter, that each group of three nucleotides along a molecule of messenger RNA directs one amino acid into a corresponding position in a protein molecule. In this section, experiments will be discussed that show which particular triplet, or triplets, of nucleotides directs each kind of amino acid into a protein. Is phenylalanine, for example, directed by -U-U-U-, or by one or more of the other sixty-four combinations? This breaking of the code has resulted from a discovery of M. W. Nirenberg and J. H. Matthaei of the National Institutes of Health. They found that, in extracts of E. coli bacteria, the natural messenger RNA could be replaced by synthetic RNA of known spelling. When this was done, abnormal proteins were formed, the spelling of which revealed the code relation of messenger RNA to protein.

Nirenberg and Matthaei made their discovery while studying the formation of proteins by extracts of E. coli bacteria. These extracts were prepared as follows: a suspension of the bacteria, which were rapidly growing, was cooled and centrifuged. The bacteria in the sediment were then broken by grinding with aluminum oxide powder. A buffer solution was added, and the mixture was centrifuged at 20,000 times the force of gravity to remove the aluminum oxide and unbroken bacteria. To this bacterial extract was added a minute quantity of the enzyme

DNAase, which breaks DNA into small fragments. The extract was further centrifuged to remove solid matter and the supernatant, which still contained the ribosomes, was dialyzed —a process which removes molecules smaller than those of proteins and nucleic acids. It was found, as expected from previous work, that when certain chemical compounds were added to this extract, it would incorporate amino acids into proteins. The formation of proteins was detected by adding radioactive amino acids, and, after incubation, precipitating the proteins and measuring their radioactivity. However, after about twenty minutes of incubation, the extracts lost the ability to form proteins. It was proved that this was because DNA had been destroyed during the preparation; if DNA was not destroyed, protein synthesis did not stop abruptly.

Nirenberg and Matthaei argued that the reason why protein synthesis ceased in the absence of DNA was because messenger RNA was destroyed after twenty minutes, and no more could be formed without DNA being there to direct its formation. They then made a beautifully simple and classical experiment of molecular biology. Could not the natural messenger RNA, which was being destroyed, be replaced by synthetic RNA of known spelling? To an extract which had lost the ability to form proteins after twenty minutes of incubation, they added ten millionths of a gram of polyuridylic acid (poly-U)—a synthetic RNA containing only nucleotides with the base uracil. When this was incubated with any radioactive amino acid except phenylalanine, little or no radioactive protein was formed. But when incubated with radioactive phenylalanine the protein precipitate was highly radioactive, and it was proved to contain only one radioactive "protein," namely, polyphenylalanine, which contains only phenylalanine. Since three nucleotides of messenger RNA appear to direct the insertion of one amino acid into a protein, they concluded that the insertion of phenylalanine is determined by three nucleotides each containing uracil. It is, therefore, possible to deduce the course of events when a gene directs the formation of a protein containing phenylalanine. The paired DNA molecules of the gene each contain three times as many nucleotides as the protein contains amino acids. One of these paired molecules has the sequence -A-A-A- at positions along the nucleotide chain which correspond to the positions of phenyl-alanine along the protein chain. Under the influence of the enzyme RNA polymerase, messenger RNA is formed in contact with this DNA, and contains the triplet -U-U-U- wherever the DNA contained -A-A-A-. The triplet -U-U-U- somehow directs phenylalanine into the protein. Hence, the code for phenylalanine is -A-A-A- on the gene, and -U-U-U- on the messenger RNA.

Since 1961, when Niremberg and Matthaei announced their dis-covery, many other experiments by them and by S. Ochoa and his colleagues at New York University have been made on the same lines. Synthetic RNA can be prepared containing more than one of the four nucleotides. The precise spelling of the molecules in any sample of this synthetic RNA is unknown and, in fact, the spelling of one molecule differs from the next, because the nucleotides are arranged in the molecules more or less at random. Nevertheless, if the relative numbers of the dif-ferent nucleotides in a sample are known, the frequency with which the different triplets occur can be calculated. This fre-quency is then correlated with the relative amounts of the different amino acids which are incorporated into protein by the RNA. In this way, triplets have been discovered for each kind of amino acid, although the order of the nucleotides in the triplets is not always known. Thus, a triplet which directs threonine contains A, A, and C but their order is unknown.

A number of questions have arisen concerning these code rela-tions which are now able to be answered. First, the four nucleo-tides of RNA can be arranged in sixty-four triplets, whereas only twenty amino acids occur in proteins. Do only twenty triplets direct amino acids, or can an amino acid be directed by more than one triplet? In the experiments of Niremberg and others, a number of amino acids have been found to be directed by more than one triplet, and it appears that most of the sixty-four direct amino acids. Second, does one particular triplet ever direct more than one amino acid? All triplets which have been studied, except one, have been found to direct only one amino acid. The exception is -U-U-U- which directs small amounts of leucine as well as phenylalanine, although it is doubtful whether it does this to a significant extent in the living cell. The answer to this question therefore appears to be, in effect, "No." Third, are the same amino acids directed by the same triplets in every living organism? The few experiments which have been done on extracts of mammalian tissues show that the amino acids which have been studied are directed by the same triplets as in *E. coli*. Hence, we find once again that organisms which are widely separated in their structure and ancestry have nevertheless all retained the chemical reactions of their common ancestor in their cells.

6 TRANSFER RNA

In this section we shall consider precisely how the nucleotides of messenger RNA guide amino acids into proteins of the correct spelling. How, for example, do three nucleotides with the bases -U-U-U- cause the insertion of phenylalanine into a protein? We know that the messenger RNA becomes attached to the ribosomes. Do the amino acids assemble in a row on the surface of the messenger RNA and link together to form a protein under the influence of an enzyme? Does the triplet -U-U-U- have some particular shape against which phenylalanine molecules fit neatly, while those of the other amino acids do not, and do the other triplets each have a shape against which only one of the other nineteen amino acids will fit neatly? Such a mechanism seems improbable. The actual mechanism is far more elegant—and was predicted in outline by F. H. C. Crick.

What molecule, in particular, will a triplet of nucleotides with, say, the bases -U-U-U- attract? The obvious answer is a nucleic acid molecule containing a triplet of nucleotides with the bases -A-A-A- in an exposed position, which would be attracted by hydrogen bonding. If phenylalanine was attached to such a molecule it would, therefore, become held on the correct region of the messenger RNA. Suppose that the adjacent triplet of nucleotides on the messenger RNA carried the bases -C-C-C- which is the code for proline. This would attract a nucleic acid molecule with the bases -G-G-G- in an exposed position. If proline was attached to such a molecule it would be held on the messenger RNA in the correct position beside phenylalanine. Evidence will be given in this section that RNA molecules of this kind, which are specific for different amino acids, do exist in free solution in living cells, and are responsible for the transport of amino acids to ribosomes. These molecules are known as transfer RNA. In effect each acts as an adaptor which gives an amino acid the right shape for fitting in the correct position on the messenger RNA of the ribosomes. The amino acids, which become arranged

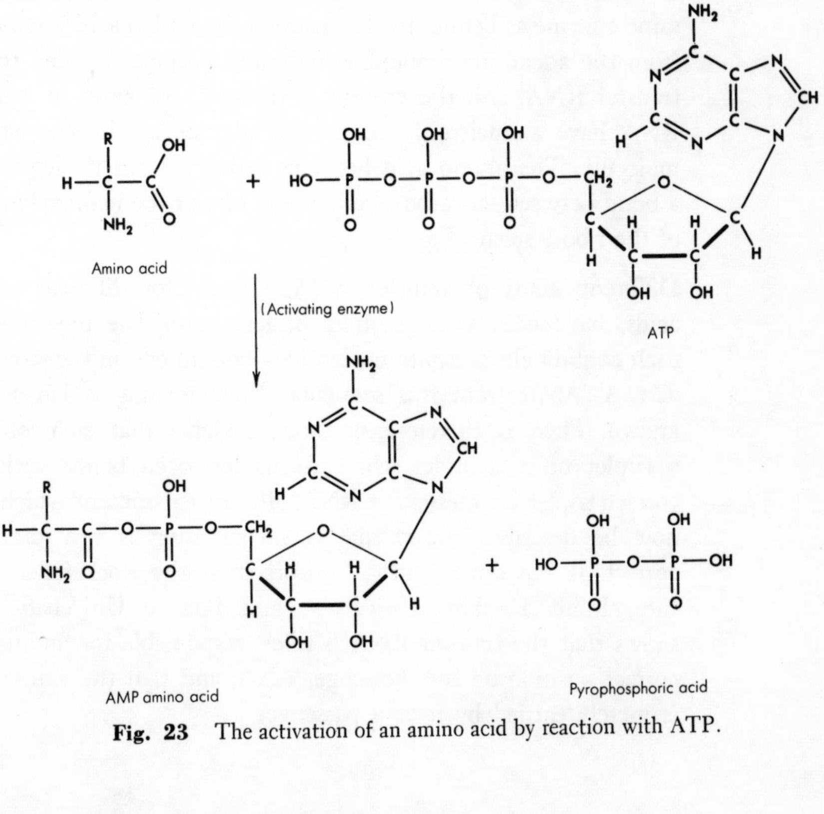

Fig. 23 The activation of an amino acid by reaction with ATP.

in this way in the correct order, are then linked together into a protein of the correct spelling, under the influence of one or more enzymes.

Transfer RNA, and also the reactions by which amino acids become attached to it, were largely discovered by M. B. Hoagland of Harvard University. Each amino acid first reacts with adenosine triphosphate (ATP), catalyzed by an enzyme—the "activating enzyme"—which is specific for that amino acid. The amino acid becomes attached by its carboxyl group to the innermost of the three phosphoric acid groups of ATP, the other two being eliminated as pyrophosphoric acid. The compound which is formed has the structure shown in Fig. 23, page 121. This compound never becomes separated from the enzyme, but immediately reacts with a molecule of the transfer RNA which is specific for the particular amino acid, the reaction being catalyzed by the same enzyme as before. In this reaction the amino acid is removed from the adenosine monophosphate and becomes bonded to the transfer RNA, and the enzyme is released. All kinds of transfer RNA have a nucleotide containing adenine at the end of the molecule. The amino acid becomes linked to this nucleotide by a bond between its carboxyl group and one of the hydroxyl groups of the ribose sugar (Fig. 24).

Different kinds of transfer RNA, specific for different amino acids, have been isolated more or less pure. The molecules of each contain about eighty nucleotides, and all end in the sequence -C-C-A. Apart from this sequence, their spelling is largely unknown. There is, therefore, no direct evidence that each contains a triplet of nucleotides which forms hydrogen bonds with the correct triplet on messenger RNA. But an experiment which will now be described shows that this conclusion is very probably correct. It was done jointly, by workers at the Rockefeller Institute, Johns Hopkins University, and Purdue University, and shows that the transfer RNA is solely responsible for finding the correct position on the messenger RNA, and that the amino acid is merely carried by it as a passenger.

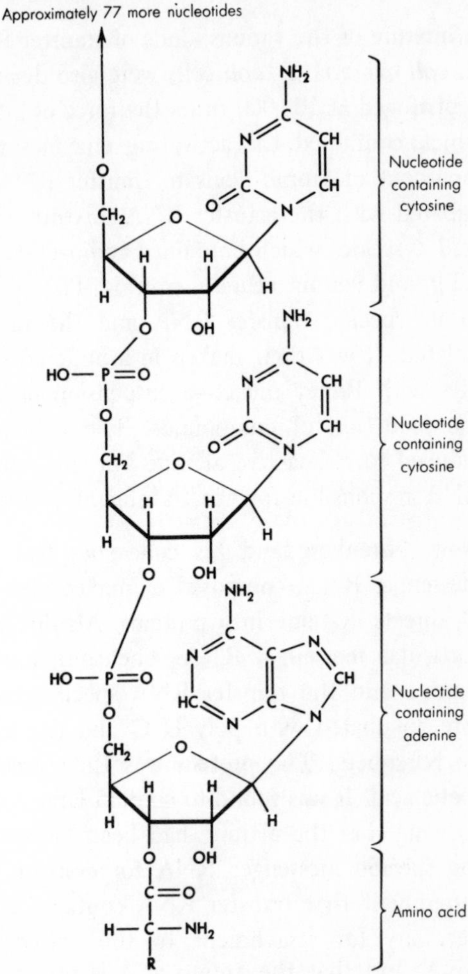

Fig. 24 Compound formed between amino acid and transfer RNA. Although transfer RNA molecules for different amino acids have different structures, they all end in the sequence -C-C-A.

In this experiment the amino acid, cysteine, was linked to its specific transfer RNA, and was then converted to the amino acid alanine, without altering the transfer RNA. It was found that the transfer RNA still behaved in protein synthesis as if it were attached to cysteine. The experiment was performed as follows.

A mixture of the various kinds of transfer RNA was isolated from *E. coli* bacteria. *E. coli* cells were also disintegrated in buffer and centrifuged at 100,000 times the force of gravity to give an extract which contained the activating enzymes which catalyze the attachment of amino acids to transfer RNA. This extract was incubated with the transfer RNA mixture and some of the amino acid cysteine, which contained radioactive carbon, together with ATP, and certain other chemicals. The cysteine became attached to its specific transfer RNA and the resulting compound was isolated. It was then shaken in a buffered solution for thirty minutes with Raney nickel—a suspension of nickel which catalyzes the reduction of compounds. The radioactive cysteine became reduced to radioactive alanine but this remained attached to the RNA responsible for the transfer of cysteine.

Now, Nirenberg and his colleagues had shown that synthetic messenger RNA, composed of nucleotides with the bases U and G, directs cysteine into proteins. Alanine is not directed by this particular messenger RNA. The compound between radioactive alanine and the transfer RNA specific for cysteine, was, therefore, incubated with poly U G and the extracts of *E. coli* used by Nirenberg. The protein was then precipitated with trichloracetic acid. It was found to contain large amounts of radioactivity, showing that the alanine had been incorporated into protein by the specific messenger RNA for cysteine. It is clear from this experiment that transfer RNA contains all the chemical groups necessary for attachment to the correct triplet in messenger RNA, and that the amino acid is not involved.

Further evidence that transfer RNA molecules act in this way, as amino acid adaptors, comes from experiments of S. Benzer and his colleagues. In the last section, it was mentioned that more than one triplet of nucleotides on messenger RNA can direct one kind of amino acid into proteins. Leucine is directed both by a triplet containing the nucleotides U, U, and G, and by one containing U, U, and C. There are also two kinds of transfer RNA which are specific for leucine. Benzer's experiments show that when leucine is linked to one kind of transfer RNA it is directed into proteins only by synthetic messenger RNA containing U and C. When linked to the other kind it is directed only by RNA containing U and G. Again, it is clear that when the compound between transfer RNA and an amino acid becomes bound by messenger RNA, it is the transfer RNA and not the amino acid which selects the correct triplet. The most obvious way in which transfer RNA can select the correct triplet is to have three nucleotides in an exposed position which will form hydrogen bonds with each of the nucleotides of the triplet on messenger RNA. But it still remains to be proved conclusively that this is the mechanism.

It will now be clear how important the specific hydrogen bonding between nucleotides containing A and those containing T or U is to life, and between nucleotides containing G and those containing C. The ability of genes to form precise self-copies is based on this specific hydrogen bonding. So is the ability of genes to send precise replicas of themselves into the cytoplasm in the form of messenger RNA. So also is the ability of messenger RNA to assemble amino acids into proteins of the correct spelling. It will be seen in the next section that another fundamental process in living cells may be founded on this hydrogen bonding, namely, the regulation of one gene by another.

7 REGULATOR GENES

We have seen that the function of many genes is to direct the formation of a protein which underlies a unit character, and we have discussed some of the chemical reactions by which this occurs. In recent years it has become clear from the work of F. Jacob and J. Monod, of the Pasteur Institute in Paris, that the primary function of many genes in E. coli bacteria is not to direct the formation of such proteins, but to regulate the action of those genes that do so. These "regulator" genes act by forming molecules which can inhibit the action of the "structural" genes which control inherited characters.

The first regulator gene to be clearly demonstrated was one in
E. coli which regulates the action of two genes which control the
formation of two specific proteins. The proteins are the enzyme
β-galactosidase which catalyzes the breakdown of the sugar lactose,
and another enzyme which catalyzes the absorption of lactose
into the bacterial cell. In normal bacteria, these enzymes are
formed only when lactose, or a related compound, is present in
the growth solution. But strains of E. coli in which the regulator
gene is defective produce the enzyme whether lactose is present
or not. In the absence of lactose, the regulator gene, therefore,
stops the other two genes from functioning, and hence, confers
on the cell the added refinement of only forming enzymes concerned in the breakdown of lactose, when lactose is there to be
broken down.

Part of the evidence that the regulator gene produces a compound which can inhibit the other two genes, comes from the
following elegant experiment of Jacob and Monod. There is also,
other comprehensive evidence that cannot be given here. It will
be remembered from an earlier chapter that certain strains of
E. coli will undergo conjugation, in which a chromosome passes
from a "male" cell into a "female." For their experiments Jacob
and Monod used a female strain in which both the gene controlling β-galactosidase formation, and the regulator gene, were
defective. These bacteria could not form β-galactosidase, even in
the presence of lactose. The male strain had both these genes intact, and, therefore, formed the enzyme provided lactose was
present.

Cultures of both strains were grown in the absence of lactose,
and were mixed and incubated at 37°C. It was known that the
bacteria would rapidly conjugate, and that after about twenty
minutes both the β-galactosidase and the regulator gene would
pass from the male cells into the female. Every few minutes
samples of the culture were assayed for their content of β-galactosidase. As expected, for the first twenty minutes, little of the
enzyme was formed, since the female cells were unable to form it,

and the male cells could do so only in the presence of lactose, or a related compound. The question of interest was, what would happen when the two genes from each male cell passed into a female, since this might give a clue as to how the regulator gene acts. It was found that soon after twenty minutes these cells started to produce β-galactosidase rapidly although no lactose was in the solution. Hence, the β-galactosidase gene had immediately become active, whereas the regulator gene had not. However, sixty minutes later production of the enzyme ceased, and would only begin again if lactose, or a related compound, was added to the solution. Hence, the regulator gene was now acting. It appears highly probable that during this sixty minutes, some compound was made, under the influence of the regulator gene, which inhibited the β-galactosidase gene unless lactose was present.

It has been shown that this inhibtor formed by the regulator gene acts by preventing the formation of messenger RNA by the genes which it inhibits. The composition of the inhibitor, and precisely how it is formed, are still unknown. It is possible that it contains RNA that becomes attached to the DNA of the inhibited genes by hydrogen bonding between A and T, or U, and between G and C. It is also possible that it contains a protein which can combine with lactose, and that when so combined the compound ceases to inhibit. These investigations are at a very early stage but they appear to be of extreme importance. In higher organisms, cells of different tissues contain different kinds of proteins showing that different genes are active in each tissue. It is hoped that the experiments on E. coli will give a clue as to how genes are regulated in higher organisms, and possibly a clue as to the cause of cancer which appears to result from the uncontrolled action of genes.

8 EPILOGUE

We have seen that heredity in all organisms is founded on cellular heredity—the ability of cells to form like cells by division. We are now, finally, in a position to outline the chemical basis of this process. It will be illustrated by an idealized situation: a bacterial cell which divides to give two daughter cells each of which then grows until it reaches exactly the size and composition of the parent cell. At division, each daughter cell receives exactly half the DNA molecules of the parent, and roughly half of the molecules of every other compound. The number of molecules of each compound must now double as each daughter cell grows to the parental size. The number of DNA molecules doubles by each pair forming self-copies, probably by the mechanism of Watson and Crick. Few, if any, other molecules form self-copies. DNA molecules direct the formation of molecules of messenger RNA and also, it appears from recent work, of those of transfer RNA and the structural RNA of ribosomes. Messenger RNA directs the formation of protein molecules of identical structure to those already present. Most of these proteins are enzymes and they catalyze the formation of many other molecules, such as those of carbohydrates and lipids, from molecules of nutrients absorbed from outside the cell. Certain other molecules whose number must also double, such as those of water, are simply absorbed from outside as the cell grows. While it is possible in this way to understand how two daughter cells can grow until they have the size and chemical composition of the parent, it is not yet understood how the newly formed molecules become grouped into the correct structures, such as ribosomes and cell membrane.

The inheritance of Mendelian unit characters by multicellular organisms is founded on cellular heredity of this kind, modified by differentiation. In these organisms, cells usually divide to give daughter cells, which differ slightly from one another in chemical composition. By a series of such divisions, cells as different as a nerve cell and a red blood cell are produced from a single fertilized egg. How the basic process of cellular heredity, which was outlined for the bacterial cell, is modified to bring about differentiation is an important unsolved problem of molecular biology. It must depend in some way on the suppression and activation of genes. After a cell division, certain genes must become activated or suppressed in one daughter cell which are not activated or suppressed in the other. This process results in the controlled appearance of new molecules, and disappearance of old ones, but precisely how it is brought about is unknown. Nevertheless, the inheritance of Mendelian unit characters can be understood on these principles. Red and white flower color in peas, for example, results from a restricted group of cells in the adult organism forming, or not forming, a colored pigment. Each of these cells contains a pair of genes which control flower color. These genes must have been replicated at every cell division between the fertilized egg and the cells of the flower, but have only become active in the mature plant.

A query arises in this connection. We have concluded that the function of most genes is to direct the formation of a specific protein. Are we to assume that the form in which every Mendelian unit character appears is the result of the formation of a protein of specific structure? Does a pea plant produce flowers at the end of the stem merely because a protein of a certain chain length and spelling is formed in certain cells, and produce flowers along the stem when this protein is absent or misspelled? There is little direct evidence on this point but the answer is almost certainly, "Yes," for it is difficult to conceive of DNA having more than the two primary chemical functions which have been discovered, namely, to direct its own self-copying, and to direct the formation of RNA which, if it is messenger RNA, will in turn direct the formation of proteins. Dominant genes, therefore, are those which produce, in certain cells of an organism, protein molecules of a certain chain length and spelling. Recessive genes are those which cause the formation of no protein or of a protein of markedly different spelling. When both genes of a pair are recessive, so that the protein which produces the dominant form of the character is absent, the recessive form appears. At first sight, it may seem surprising that whether peas are tall or short, whether their seeds are round or wrinkled, whether their flowers are red or white, and so on, should each be decided by the structure of a protein. It is in fact no more surprising than that each should ultimately be determined by the structure of DNA.

The task of this book—to show how inherited differences between one living organism and another are founded on differences in the structure of chemical molecules—is, therefore, completed. What are other main problems of molecular biology? There is first the problem of differentiation which is probably founded on chemical processes which are modifications of those that have been discussed in this book. It is likely that this foundation will be discovered within the next ten years. Many biochemists assume that all the basic problems of inheritance and development will then be solved. Biologists point out that this is not so, and that biochemists have a blind spot. Genetics, they claim, will not be fully solved until we understand, at least in outline, how the formation of a protein in certain cells can give rise to such structural characters as round seed and tall plants in peas. Differentiation will not be fully solved until we understand not only how cells of differing composition can result from the controlled activation and suppression of genes, but also how this differing composition can in turn result in the cells assuming a typical shape, and becoming grouped into ordered structures, such as liver, kidney and lungs. In other words, the forces involved in the formation of cell structures, and in the grouping of cells, are not yet understood.

Apart from these problems there is another area of biology which may be founded on differences in the structure of large molecules: the function of the brain. The brain receives and sends out information largely by electrical impulses, based on the movement of sodium and potassium ions across cell membranes. But this electrical activity appears to be evanescent and memories must be stored in some other way. A number of workers in this area suggest that one memory is distinguished from another by differences in the structure of RNA molecules. The evidence for this is slight, and memories may in fact be distinguished by different patterns being formed by molecules of identical structure. But whatever the answer, the brain is a fascinating subject for study and poses a problem similar to that which was posed by the living cell: do all the manifestations of the brain result solely from the interaction of its component parts according to the normal laws of chemistry and physics? Most psychologists believe that the answer is, "Yes," and many philosophers claim that any other answer is impossible. But there are eminent physiologists who believe that the answer is, "No." They believe that in higher animals there is in fact a "ghost" which operates the biochemical machine by redirecting the normal course of physical events. The problem appears overwhelmingly difficult, but so did the problem of the chemical basis of heredity fifty years ago.

Selected
Readings

CHAPTER 1

Fruton, J. S. and S. Simmonds. *General Biochemistry*. 2nd ed. New York: John Wiley & Sons, Inc., 1958. *An advanced textbook of biochemistry with good discussions of the structure of proteins and nucleic acids.*

Perutz, M. F. "Some recent advances in molecular biology." *Endeavour*. **17**: 190, 1958. *Describes the use of X-ray diffraction in determining the structure of nucleic acids and proteins.*

CHAPTER 2

Colowick, S. P. and N. O. Kaplan, eds. *Methods in Enzymology.* Volume 1. New York: Academic Press, 1955. *Contains practical instructions for separating components of cells.*

Davidson, J. N. *The Biochemistry of the Nucleic Acids.* 4th ed. New York: John Wiley & Sons, Inc., 1960. *Contains a clear account of the structure of nucleic acids and their distribution within cells.*

Swanson, C. P. *The Cell.* 2nd ed. Englewood Cliffs, New Jersey: Prentice-Hall, Inc., 1964. *Contains a clear account of the structure of living cells and of cell division.*

CHAPTER 3

Iltis, H. *Life of Mendel.* Trans. E. and C. Paul. London: George Allen & Unwin Ltd., 1932. *A fascinating account of Mendel's life by a scientist from Brünn who spoke to many of his relatives and friends.*

Sinnott, E. W., L. C. Dunn and T. Dobzhansky. *Principles of Genetics.* 5th ed. New York: McGraw-Hill, Inc., 1958. *The best comprehensive textbook of genetics—advanced but readable.*

CHAPTERS 4, 5, & 6

Anfinsen, C. B. *The Molecular Basis of Evolution.* New York: John Wiley & Sons, Inc., 1959. *A discussion of the chemical basis of genetics and its relation to evolution.*

Beadle, G. W. "Genes and Chemical Reactions in Neurospora." *Science.* **129:** 1715, 1959. *Nobel prize lecture given in Stockholm and describing the development of the "one gene—one enzyme" hypothesis.*

Jacob, F. and J. Monod. "Genetic Regulatory Mechanisms in the Synthesis of Proteins." *Journal of Molecular Biology.* **3:** 318, 1961. *A discussion of the evidence for regulator genes, and their mode of action.*

Kornberg, A. "Biologic Synthesis of Deoxyribonucleic Acid." *Science.* **131:** 1503, 1960. *Nobel prize lecture describing the self-copying of DNA "in the test-tube."*

Perutz, M. F. *Proteins and Nucleic Acids.* Amsterdam: Elsevier Publishing Co., 1962. *An advanced account of recent work on the structure and biosynthesis of proteins and nucleic acids by a man who has been awarded the Nobel Prize for his work on the subject.*

Strauss, B. S. *An Outline of Chemical Genetics.* Philadelphia: W. B. Saunders Co., 1960. *A clear account of recent work on the chemical basis of genetics.*

Index